The Longdown LOCKDOWN

Farmer Bryan

First published in the United Kingdom
in 2023 by Ceratopia Books,
2 Solent Road, Dibden Purlieu, Southampton, SO45 4QG

www.ceratopiabooks.co.uk

Text © 2023 Bryan Pass
Illustrations © 2023 Simon Chadwick

A catalogue record for this book is available
from the British Library.

ISBN 978-1-8384432-8-3

Printed in the UK.

www.ceratopiabooks.co.uk

1.

"It's all hyped up by the press; that's never going to happen. How could they lock down the entire country just because a flu virus is going round? These journalists need to get a real job and stop scaremongering! I need to get out and check on Abbie to see if she's calving yet as that's more important to me at the moment."

It was late March, 2020, and, yes, I was getting agitated by the way the media were portraying the severity of the virus that everyone was talking about as we watched the news at ten o'clock.

Dawn, my wife, looked at me as I headed for the door. "But if they do put the country in lockdown, what will happen to the farm?" she asked. "How will we survive? What will happen to all the animals and the season ticket holders that have already paid for this year? How on earth will we be able to refund them, with no income coming in? How will we pay all the invoices that are sat on your desk; have you given that a thought?"

"Of course I have, but don't worry yourself with all that rubbish! It simply won't be happening. Give it a week or two, it will have all blown over and we'll be back to normal," I curtly replied.

I knew that Dawn had watched me as I'd listened to Robert Peston expressing his political views. She had rightly judged from my expressions, and my outburst at the telly, that I was becoming increasingly worried about the whole situation and was not very good at hiding it.

Jess, my very faithful border collie, excitedly jumped up at me as I headed towards the door. She nuzzled her nose into my face as I tried to put my wellies on, and I pushed her away as she placed her foot on to my knee, staring at me affectionately with those piercing eyes. It's amazing how an animal can recognise your mood no matter how hard you try to conceal it.

As we walked towards the barn where Abbie, our Friesian cow, had started to calve, Jess kept to my side and continuously rubbed alongside me, trying her utmost to gain my attention. The more I tried to ignore her, the more determined she was to catch my eye.

Abbie was lying down in the corner of the pen whilst the other cows watched over her. There was no sign of a calf as yet but she was beginning to strain a little.

As I put my hand in to check if there were any feet ready to come out, she decided to stand and bolt for the gate, leaving me in a heap on the floor. She turned and faced me, giving a growling snort as I attempted to move out of the building. Abbie was now towering above me, pawing at the ground. When a cow giving birth reacts like this, it's an indication that they are in pain and this can be a very dangerous situation.

Jess started to bark, which attracted the angry cow to her, and I managed to crawl under the fence to safety. Jess was immediately there, licking my face and wagging her tail repeatedly.

"Come on, girl, we'll need to check on her again later as the calf is not ready to come out yet. Another late night," I sighed to Jess. "Who would be a farmer?"

As I lay in bed, watching the minutes roll over on the digital clock, my brain was full of solutions on how we would cope if the farm was forced to close, combined with who I should call if I needed a hand to pull the calf out at this unearthly time of night.

The clock seemed to brighten up at one o'clock, the time that I felt would be right to go and check on Abbie calving. Jess was at the door, waiting, as I pulled on my overalls, the chill of the early morning persuading me to head back into the house to put on my coat, too.

Jess ran ahead as we walked towards the shed where Abbie was now straining, and it was quite apparent that she was struggling to get the calf to squeeze through her pelvis. The front legs were now dangling lifelessly from her tail end and its head was jammed. I knew I had no time to waste if I was to get the calf out alive. Luckily, I had the calving ropes and a bucket of water – which had now become cold – next to the pen.

As I scrubbed my hands and arms with the chill water, trying to create some lather, Abbie stood up, enabling me to secure the ropes on to the calf's spindly legs. As she strained, I pulled harder, but to no avail; there was absolutely no movement. I now pushed the head backwards to release the pressure and lubricated around the base, enabling me to slide the head to one side. This allowed me to squeeze my fingers through the narrow gap to reach the crown of the calf's head. This meant I was then able to pull the head downwards as she contracted. But, as a consequence, my fingers were now jammed tight against her pelvis bones.

After five or more minutes, which seemed like a lifetime at that early morning hour, the ropes that were latched on to the legs and tied around my waist suddenly moved and the calf started to come forward. With Abbie now pushing with all her might, the shoulders slipped out, followed by the hips.

As the calf dropped on to the straw, it looked lifeless, with mucus covering its nostrils. Quickly, I managed to find a stiff piece of straw and gently pushed it up the calf's nostrils, rubbing its lung cavity at the same time. Fortunately, it didn't take long before there was a sign of slight breathing motion over its rib cage.

As the steam bellowed from the calf's wet body as it met with the cold morning air, Abbie stood up and headed directly towards the calf. I knew this was the time for me to exit; my job was completed as she licked the calf with her rough tongue. This soon encouraged the calf to raise its head. Just a few gentle coughs were an indication that the lungs were working well.

Completely exhausted, I leant across the rails of the pen and watched as mother and son bonded. Jess nuzzled against my boots, watching with intent as the calf clumsily staggered to his feet, swaying his 36kg of weight across the straw bed.

I, on the other hand, headed back to the farmhouse to try to catch another hour or two of sleep.

THE LONGDOWN LOCKDOWN

2.

While listening to the five o'clock news whilst drinking my first brew of the day, my heart stopped as the newscaster confidently informed the listeners that the entire country would be put into a lockdown very shortly. "There is no alternative," he continued. I swore at the radio as I put my overalls back on to go out and check on Abbie and her calf.

"How on earth can they put the whole country into a lockdown?" I questioned Jess as we walked across the yard. "That's just nonsense and scaremongering," I continued. Jess knew from my body language that I was not happy. She bounded in front of me to the pen where Abbie and her calf were standing. The calf and mother both looked incredibly well considering what they had been through just a few hours previously.

I pushed the calf to Abbie's teats and squirted some of the warm milk into his mouth to encourage him to drink. Within seconds, he latched on and I left him suckling merrily. I could take some comfort from knowing that he was getting some vital colostrum.

Each morning I had been listening to the news, observing the daily Covid-19 cases and their locations. It was soon apparent that this problem was not going away, and it was spreading quickly.

Having lived through several 'Foot and Mouth' outbreaks, witnessing the devastation they caused throughout the farming industry as animals with cloven feet were destroyed on farms throughout the country to help stop the virus from spreading, the memories of listening to distraught farmers still haunt me to this day.

I recall the Swine Fever outbreak which swept through herds of pigs nationwide in 2009 and even the Avian Flu, which led to the slaughter of so many birds. Although these diseases never reached our farm, the precautions and consequences did. We were now heading for a similar situation with this dreaded virus, but this time it would affect every human being in the country in some form or another.

I am convinced that this is Mother's Nature way of dealing with our over-population problem.

As Liza, our publicity manager, and I sat at the kitchen table to discuss how we would handle the inevitable lockdown, it was announced on the radio that there would be an important announcement from the Prime Minister, Boris Johnson.

A chill went through my body as I reached out to turn up the radio. The gravity of the situation made it feel akin to Winston Churchill announcing the outbreak of World War Two. The slow-speaking sombre voice of Boris echoed through the kitchen as he gave the grave news that the entire country would be put into lockdown. As much as we had expected it, both of us looked at each other with disbelief as the reality set in.

We needed to make some decisions as soon as practicably possible: what would happen to our dedicated staff, how would we find the money to feed the animals, how would we compensate our season ticket holders who had already purchased their annual passes for the 2020 season?

Then there were our suppliers who would require payment for the goods that had already been purchased for the Tea Room and Gift Shop.

My brain was crammed full with all these concerns.

Both Liza and I are very positive-minded people but, on this occasion, we looked at each other with blank expressions. "I'm sure there will be a way out of this," Liza said quietly.

I was not convinced.

As Dawn and I discussed our future plans over breakfast, we were both very concerned about what would happen to the staff that we employed. Some of them had young families, others were living with elderly parents and grandparents, and were now worried about the possibility of spreading the virus to them. Dawn and I needed to get to grips with how we were going to afford to pay the wages if we had no income coming in.

"Unfortunately, there's no alternative: we'll have to lay off all the staff until we can reopen," I said, regretfully.

"What about this furlough payment people are talking about?" Dawn quizzed.

"The government won't pay that back for at least three or four months and we simply won't have enough money to pay that amount in the first place – and we've already exceeded our overdraft." I was feeling the anger coming through my voice as I slid my chair across the floor.

This was something I was really not looking forward to doing, but we needed to tell them as soon as possible. As we headed to the Tea Room, I said, "We had better get all the staff that are working today together and tell them the bad news."

My daughter Kerry called all the staff on the radios and asked them to come to the Tea Room for an urgent meeting. As I looked around the room, listening to the chatter and laughter from all our team, you could have been forgiven for believing that they were unaware of what was happening in the wider world outside. I'm quite sure they weren't expecting what I was about to tell them. I cleared my throat with a little cough, then anxiously sipped at my tea from a paper cup, watching the team looking at me in anticipation.

"Well, I guess you know why you've been called in," I clumsily started. "The country is being put into lockdown. Unfortunately that means we'll have no alternative but to close the farm. This means that we're unable to offer you any employment until the lockdown is over."

I paused for a while and watched the stunned expressions on each of their faces before continuing. "Hopefully you all realise that this is completely out of our control. We simply don't have enough money in the bank to pay your wages." By this point I was now struggling to stop my emotions taking over.

Luckily, Kerry looked across and took control. "Oh, well, everyone – it looks as though we're all going to have a long holiday! Hopefully the sun will shine long enough for us all to get a tan!"

This lightened the atmosphere in the room and gave me enough time to compose myself. I took over again, explaining to the team that I would be discussing the arrangements with Tammy, our HR consultant. We would speak to each member of our team individually to discuss any future arrangements.

"If I get another job in the care home that mum works in, will it be okay for me to come back when you reopen?" Aimee, one of the livestock assistants, asked.

"Absolutely! And that applies to you all. If you can get another job, please do, as we really don't know how along it will be before we will reopen," was my response.

"How long will we be laid off for?" asked Mike, another livestock assistant.

"Until the farm can reopen," Kerry responded.

Dawn could sense the anguish in my voice and calmly took over: "As you know, we really don't have any other options. We'll do our utmost to keep the farm afloat until you are all able to return. We've been through a lot together yet, each time, we've always bounced back. Yes, this time is far more serious, but I know that we'll keep the farm going."

These few words seemed to reassure the team that we would pull through this. Without exception, each and every one of our team fully understood our dilemma and were only too keen to support us. If only they knew the negative vibes going through my brain at that time.

As we headed back to the house, I explained to Kerry and Dawn that there were too many animals on the farm and the three of us, plus my granddaughter Charley, simply wouldn't be able look after them all ourselves. Ideally we would need some help. And that meant keeping some of the livestock staff on board. The question was, could we afford them?

"Hollie has already told me that she'll be in as usual even if she's not going to get paid," said Kerry. "I know other staff will support you, Dad, so let's not worry about that at the moment. We have more serious things to consider."

That was all very well, but I was all too aware that everyone had bills to pay. If we had to keep a staff member or two on, I wanted to be able to pay them.

My phone call to Tammy, our HR consultant, made me feel like a fish out of water as she tried to explain the possibilities of furlough. To me, this was a completely new word, one that had never reached my limited vocabulary.

Tammy assured me that "the government will ensure that each of your staff will receive 80% of their wage, however you will have to pay this money to them upfront and it may be months before it gets paid into your account. You will need to pay their National Insurance and any pension contributions, too."

"So, in order to keep everyone on, I'll need to fork out over £45,000 before I can claim any of it back!" My hand was shaking as I spoke.

"I fully understand that," Tammy interrupted, "but let's not be hasty. You can simply lay off the staff until you're in a position to pay the furlough money. There are going to be grants and assistance from the government on this matter, so let's review it on a regular basis," she calmly concluded.

It looked as if my hope to keep some livestock staff on to help us out was a non-starter. Myself, Dawn, Kerry and Charley would just have to cope.

Reams and reams of guidance and updates were now clogging my inbox on the computer; if only I had time to read it all, let alone understand its content. Luckily for me, I was surrounded by a team of dedicated and well educated advisors and staff who helped me understand and explained the complexity of it all.

Liz, who had been the backbone of our business, working in our small office, helped to sort through the emails and dealt with the enquiries that were flowing in. It was a hard moment for me to inform Liz that, unfortunately, we were going to have to lay her off as well.

In her very calm way, she smiled and said: "You have my number; I'm only a phone call away, should you need a hand. And please don't worry about me! I have enough to keep me occupied. But please promise me that you or Dawn will contact me if you require any help at all."

When Liz walked out of the office, I felt completely lost as I stared at the large pile of paperwork, all neatly presented with yellow sticky notes, which Liz had written priorities upon.

I slumped into the high-backed leather chair, knowing that now I was on my own, dealing with all the phone calls, emails and post. None of which, I hasten to add, I'm very good at.

Thumbing through the top layer of folders, which contained invoices due to be paid immediately, I felt my heart racing. In a fit of uncharacteristic rage, I threw the bulky folders across the desk, strewing them across the office floor. "How on earth are we going to get through this," I shouted to the empty room.

THE LONGDOWN LOCKDOWN

3.

It seemed very strange as I closed the gates after the staff had gone home on the Friday evening. After chaining the car park gates together, wondering how long they would be closed before visitors could return again, I called Liza from my mobile. I explained that we'd need to change the website and update all our social media platforms to inform everyone that the farm would be closed until further notice.

"Oh no," Liza said. "Why so soon? I believe Marwell and Paultons are still open. You realise that we'll miss out on Mother's Day?"

"It would be completely irresponsible to open when the Government has insisted that all public places should close," I replied. "We also have to consider our staff. We really don't wish to put them at risk from the virus. I'm going to check with Wayne to see if he's happy to keep the Farm Shop open. That, at least, is providing essential goods."

"Then, hopefully, it will only be for a few weeks and things will get back to normal," Liza added.

As I walked around the farm, later that evening, I noticed that Abbie's calf was lying motionless in the corner. Abbie was towering over him.

Climbing into the pen, I pulled the calf's head around. I could see that he was dehydrated and in desperate need of some fluid. Abbie, herself, was also showing signs of stress and not chewing the cud. A closer look swiftly pointed to the problem. It was obvious that her udder was extremely swollen.

Some further investigation was needed, including taking her temperature. When I removed the thermometer from her rear end, I was horrified to see it showing a temperature of over 105 degrees; there was something seriously wrong.

Without hesitation, I pulled out the mobile from my overalls and called the vet. Yes, it was going to cost more money – in fact, probably more than Abbie was worth – but there was no way I could let this friendly cow and her calf suffer.

Alex, the vet, was very quick to respond. After listening to the symptoms over the phone, he told me he would be there as soon as possible.

I then called on Hollie to assist and, judging by how quickly she arrived at the farm after travelling the five miles from home, I wouldn't have been surprised if she had received a speeding ticket.

The three of us managed to move Abbie into a corner of the pen, covered in fresh barley straw. We secured her behind a five-bar galvanised gate as Alex started to drip feed fluid into the calf to get its gut operating, pumping a cocktail of antibiotics and painkillers into its main artery.

Hollie, meanwhile, took off her coat and wrapped it round the calf, which was now shivering. Alex shook his head and gave a nod towards the young animal, indicating that there was not much hope in saving it. But Hollie caught his eye. "He will pull through. I won't let him die!" she declared.

Both Alex and I begged to differ and turned towards Abbie, but Hollie was having none of it. "I won't let him die," she repeated.

Although Abbie was still standing, we knew that she was in a serious condition. As we tried to draw milk from her swollen udder, she lashed out with her left leg, catching Alex's hand between the bars of the metal gate. Bravely, he managed to remove his hand before she gave out a second violent kick. This time, her leg went through the bars, trapping it. She started to throw her 650kg body recklessly around the pen in an attempt to remove her foot. In doing so, the gate – which the three of us were hanging, helplessly, on to – went flying into the air. Miraculously, none of us were injured although Alex was still rubbing his throbbing wrist.

Our second attempt was more successful as we managed to persuade Abbie back into the corner. The milk that we drew from her teats was now very watery and clots of blood fell on to the straw bedding. This confirmed my diagnosis that she had mastitis. As Alex and Hollie continued to strip her four teats out, with 40ml of an antibiotic cocktail being released into each quarter and another 20ml into each muscle on her back end, she seemed to realise that we were only trying to help her.

By now, the calf had lifted its head. Alex mixed up two litres of an energy solution and Hollie gently pushed a long tube down the calf's throat to enable us to drip feed the solution directly into the stomach. The determination and desperation in her voice as she comforted it proved that she simply wasn't going to give up on this little calf.

That night, sleep was hard to come by. I watched the clock flash up every hour. It seemed that I hadn't slept a wink when 4:45 lit up. Having never used an alarm to wake me in the morning, it just seemed natural to climb out of bed at this time of day.

"Do I really need to shave and shower?" I asked myself. "Guess I'm not going to see anyone today. Just the animals."

But, even though the farm wasn't open to the public, there was a colossal amount of work to do. My brain seemed ready to explode as I considered which animals could be put into the large twenty-acre field at the back of the farm. This would save on food and bedding. Unfortunately, at this time of the year, the ground was still extremely wet.

Being clay-based soil, it would take two or three weeks of dry weather before the grass began to grow. The horses had been in the field during the daytime throughout the winter months, leaving the gateways ankle deep in mud.

Soon I was walking around the farm, counting what livestock we had in the buildings and estimating how much feed, straw, and hay and shavings for bedding would be required each day. The awful reality was beginning to kick in.

The food bill for all the animals we had on the premises was now exceeding £2000 a week, bedding nearing £1000 a week. Even the hay for the horses, goats and cattle added up to over £500. With absolutely no income being generated from the farm, we would need to decide on how we were going to get through the next few weeks.

To my surprise, Hollie and Charis arrived at the farm at seven o'clock.

"Before you ask, we know that we've been laid off but there's no way that we're going to let you, Dawn, Kerry and Charley look after all these animals by yourself," they said in chorus. Although relieved, I was somewhat taken back and was not prepared for this.

"I'm sorry, girls, but there is no money in the pot to pay your wages. You had better get back in your cars and go back home." Knowing it sounded ungrateful, I apologised, trying not to show that my eyes were welling up as I opened up the pedestrian gate for them leave.

And yet, to my surprise, they completely ignored me. Instead, they strode down the yard, deliberately not turning round, with Jess bouncing alongside of them as though she was all part of the plan.

I didn't know what to do or say – just stood there foolishly as the girls hastened their pace as if to get away from me as quickly as possible.

I tracked them down in the goat barn. Working as a team, Hollie and Charis mixed up the milk for the small goat kids. They made a point of avoiding eye contact with me, chatting together as though I wasn't there at all.

Feeling somewhat foolish, I started talking: "Okay, so you don't trust me with your goats, I fully understand that. But nobody knows how long this lockdown is going to last so I really can't let you work indefinitely for nothing. I'm not even sure if the business is going to survive so we'll be in a position to reopen." The words were just pouring out clumsily. "Look, maybe you could help me decide which animals we're going to have to move off the farm – to help reduce the food bill – and then, maybe, we can find some money in the kitty to take some staff back on to help look after the animals." I felt very awkward as I tried to reason with the pair of them.

Hollie was having none of it. "Look, we would only be at home getting bored and – as you know – we all love our jobs here so we really feel that we need to help you out. We've worked out that we can survive the next four weeks without needing any wages. And that's what we are going to do. So, please, don't argue. You have enough on your plate. Let us get on and feed these goats. They're hungry; they should have had their first feed an hour ago!" Hollie, acting as spokesperson, was behaving completely out of character. It certainly left me speechless.

A short while later, as we munched on our breakfast with Kerry and Charley, Dawn and I discussed the loyalty of our staff.

"Look, they wouldn't do it if they didn't want to," Dawn told me. "And

I know that you feel embarrassed as we've never asked for help like this before. We're not getting any younger and, with the workload outside, we're going to struggle, without doubt. Remember, it's not our fault that we're in this situation. We're in a pandemic which no one would have even imagined was possible a few weeks ago. Let the girls help. We'll repay them somehow, at some point." However, Dawn's sage words weren't soothing my troubled mind.

"I just can't see a way out of this. We owe so much money, it will take years to get out of this mess! We have to accept that we cannot continue. There's only one sensible option. I'm going to declare ourselves bankrupt tomorrow. I've given this a lot of thought and this is the only way out of it!" I had been mulling this over almost constantly for some time now, but had not yet spoken it aloud. And here I was, blurting it all out over breakfast.

"Stop thinking like that," Dawn said forcefully.

"Give it a little more time, Dad," Kerry insisted. "Hopefully, then, things will all be okay."

Charley moved to my side of the kitchen table, put her arm around my shoulders and whispered in my ear: "You cannot sell the farm. I'm going to work out there for nothing, I promise. You simply cannot sell the farm." There were tears flowing from her eyes. For the second time in a couple of hours, I found myself speechless.

THE LONGDOWN LOCKDOWN

4.

"Let's turn the horses out day and night; the three cows and their calves can be turned out as well. The other calves can go back to Alan; I'll try to sell as many pigs as I possibly can. Hollie, we'll need to sell at least half your goats. All the poultry can be sold. We simply have to get this food bill down as quickly as we can." I felt I was taking control of the situation.

"Hold on, Dad," jumped in Kerry. "What happens when we reopen in a few weeks' time? We won't have any animals for our visitors to look at!"

So much for me taking control. It looked like I could be swapping one set of problems for another. And Kerry wasn't finished yet.

"Just slow down and let's think this through! You know, darn well, it's too cold at night for those animals to be turned out. There's no grass growing so you'll still need to feed them. And who's going to struggle through the mud with those heavy hay bales? If you sell all those goats, will you be able to purchase more when we re-open? I thought you said there won't be any more kids about until August?"

My mind was reeling. All of this should have been obvious to me, but such was the burden of the constant decision-making, the bleak financial situation, and the ongoing uncertainty that I wasn't seeing the bigger picture.

"I know you're worried about how we're going to get through this, Dad," said Kerry softly. "But don't be too hasty in making decisions that you may regret." It seemed like I'd have to leave the logical thinking to Kerry for a while.

One of the most time-consuming and troublesome tasks I had to deal with was ploughing through the endless stream of emails and correspondence that flooded into the farm. Sat in the office, I tried to keep to Liz's immaculate filing system. It was, by now, quite apparent that there were a lot more outstanding invoices to pay than I had anticipated.

The Gift Shop and Tea Room had ordered thousands of pounds worth of goods in preparation for the Easter holidays. On top of this, there were invoices for the building works, electrician and plumber all waiting for payment. With £30,000 in the bank, these would normally be paid at the end of the month. However, when I fumbled with the calculator, I could see the figures we owed rise in excess of £100,000, and that didn't include the £32,000 VAT demand.

Dawn and I had never been in debt before; we had always managed to pay off any invoices as they dropped on the doorstep. We had always taken pride that we did not owe anyone a penny. But that, clearly, was about to change. The overdraft arrangements would not cover the excess required. To make matters even worse, there was the prospect of another £50,000 worth of expenditure being added on to this figure that very month.

Things were looking extremely serious.

How on earth were we going to get through this?

Darren, our bank manager, was overwhelmed with requests and sent me a standard email response: "I hope to be able to look at your request in three weeks' time." I read the email with a heavy sigh. The scale of the problem facing all businesses in the country was obviously taking its toll – but a three-week wait wasn't going to help me. I needed assistance immediately.

Next I turned to Stuart, our accountant. Stuart has always been extremely supportive and encouraging, so I wasn't ready for his plain talking. He was now telling me that, perhaps, now was the time to pull the plug.

"Do you really wish to continue with so much uncertainty?" he asked me. "Of course, I'm aware that you've spent your life building up this business. Yes, you have a valuable asset, beloved by the local community. But, if this lockdown continues for more than a few weeks, you will seriously struggle."

It was hard to hear such a brutal reading of the facts. Regardless of the emotional reasons for wanting to keep going, it seemed that the financial reality was going to dictate whether we survived as Longdown Activity Farm.

"Let's review the situation in a few weeks' time," Stuart carefully advised.

Reluctantly, and with a measure of despair, all I could do was agree.

●

I was struggling to find friends in the business world to give me words of encouragement; most were telling me to either give up or stop paying any of the invoices. Brian, a good friend of mine who also happens to be a very successful businessman, called me: "Don't give up. You will get through this. Simply stop paying all your invoices, including any outstanding VAT. It will all work out in the end. Let your suppliers know that, ultimately, you will not let them down."

These were difficult words for me to hear. It just wasn't how I'd operated the business up until now and I just wasn't sure I could adopt these methods. Brian wasn't suggesting anything outrageous – it was practical advice to help us get through to the other side. But was it something I could do?

"Bryan, your suppliers know you and Dawn well enough to know that you are honest people. They will back you, I promise. They would be fools if they don't. We are all in this together and we will all need each other to get through this; hang in there."

I also phoned a friend of mine, Tim, who is a business consultant. It was time for some plain talking.

"Tim, what do you think I should do? Financially, we are ruined, but I really want to keep this business going. What would you do if you were in my position?"

"I've been thinking of you and Dawn," Tim replied. "I've been expecting your call, Bryan. If you were any other business, I would advise you to pack up as soon as possible. But, you are not a normal business. You are a hub within the community, providing so much pleasure and support to so many people. The schools and families that visit, the good work that you undertake with the groups of students with assisted needs, the advice you provide to people keeping chickens, your generosity to so many charities you have supported throughout the years – and not forgetting your wonderful staff. There is no way that you'll be able to turn your back on all this; you would regret it for the rest of your life if you gave up now. Persevere, young man. I'll support you as much as I can at absolutely no cost to you."

They were, undoubtedly, kind words, and I was grateful for them. But it was going to take more than that to see us through lockdown.

THE LONGDOWN LOCKDOWN

5.

"We have over a thousand chickens at various ages. I'll try to move these on as soon as possible," I was explaining to Wayne, the Farm Shop manager. But that wasn't what I really needed to discuss with him. "So, Wayne, are you happy in keeping the Farm Shop open? Do you think people will still want to come out to the shop when we're in a lockdown or do you think they are more likely to go to the supermarkets?"

Keeping the Farm Shop open would come with its own pros and cons, but ultimately it could be good for us and good for the community. But it all came down to Wayne.

Wayne, it seemed, had already been giving it plenty of thought. "I believe that the local residents will be happier to come to the shop rather than go into the larger supermarkets. As long as we keep to social distancing and only allow one or two families in at a time, it should be an asset to all. Also, I need the shop open to sell the poultry and pet feed as animals will still need to be fed."

"And, by opening, at least we'll have some income to pay your wages," I quickly added.

"No problem. As long as Richard is happy, we'll stay open and see how it goes," Wayne responded.

My chat with Wayne had put me into a better mood. What's more, I had some people coming to buy a few of the chickens I needed to sell. But my good humour didn't last long before I was in trouble again. This time, with my daughter.

"Dad, don't you know you're meant to be wearing a mask when you're speaking to people about chickens!" she, quite rightly, berated me.

"Personally, I think face masks and shields are a waste of time," I grouched back. "This bloomin' Covid virus is like any other virus: it's airborne. That's why we should all be getting plenty of fresh air, not hiding behind these silly cloth and paper masks! All they're doing is restricting the amount of fresh air we breath in and making everyone look silly. It gives them a false sense of security. How do you think we've managed with all the viruses that animals have? Vaccine and fresh air, that's what we should be doing! Not covering everyone up in these stupid masks!" I seemed to be on some sort of roll. "Even the government cannot decide if it's the right thing to wear them or not."

"Whoa! Okay, Dad. Get off your high horse! That's your opinion, but the experts are all saying masks should be worn. So, for once in your life, can you do as you're told. It's either that or you don't get involved with selling the chickens."

I most certainly wasn't about to let that happen. But it seemed that Kerry wasn't quite finished with me yet.

"And don't forget that you are in the vulnerable age group. Yes, you're amongst the oldies, so we need to protect you and you need to be more considerate to other people." That was a tough one to argue against. "As from now, you will have to sell your chickens from the tables that we have put out by the shop. You are not to go closer than two metres to anyone. Because, if you do, you won't be selling any chickens at all."

My stroppy daughter had spoken.

Suitably chastised, I continued to sell my chickens in the prescribed manner. And, boy, did they sell. All of a sudden, having a chicken or two at home seemed to be all the rage.

Strangely, this had a rather unexpected consequence. Lockdown had created a keeping chickens craze – we even had people driving from as far as London and Oxford to pick up two or three of these egg-laying machines – and so, before I knew it, I'd sold all of the one thousand chickens on the farm.

And people wanted more.

I found myself in the strange position of having to buy more in.

Most of our suppliers seemed to consider it reasonable to double the price due to the high demand, meaning that I would need to sell each bird at £30 or more to gain the same margin. This was just too steep for my liking.

Luckily, I found that my main supplier had had a cancellation for an order of five hundred birds and he was happy to supply them to me at the same price as normal. A positive result. You won't need to guess who I planned to keep on dealing with once the pandemic was over!

Unfortunately, when it came to chickens, not all our customers knew what they were letting themselves in for. Like any creature, a chicken needs looking after properly. I had to upset several families who told me they were going to keep the birds in their bedroom or under the tree in the garden.

Some even swore at me when I refused to let them have the chickens.

I make no apology for insisting it be done properly, and so, to ensure this happened, I came up with a solution. From then on, when anyone turned up for chickens and had not kept them before, I provided them with a copy of my book *Chickens In Your Garden: Your Essential Guide To Keeping Chickens At Home*. This, at least, gives me some reassurance that the chickens will be well looked after.

Steadily, we were settling in to the rhythms of this new routine. Deep down, it still felt like a losing battle, and there were still plenty of problems, both big and small, to contend with. Some, looking back, don't seem so huge now, but that doesn't mean they didn't cause me a headache.

Such as my monthly newsletter to our season ticket holders.

I had been sat glaring at the computer screen for far too long, considering what to write. How could I type something in a positive manner when my mind was full of negativity.

Instead, I picked up my mobile and called Liza, who had now become my sounding board. "I'm sorry it's so late, Liza, but I'm trying to put a few words together and nothing I consider writing sounds interesting. In fact, it all just sounds depressing. I'm thinking I should leave it for this month." My exhausted tone seemed to echo over the phone.

There's a reason Liza's my sounding board. She's not afraid to tell me when I'm wrong and she nurtures and helps grow any ideas that are right. Sometimes, she's just the tonic I need.

"Bryan, you're tired and emotionally drained," she correctly pointed out. "Turn off your computer, have a large Scotch and go to bed. When you're ready, you'll be able to put words together like you always do. And, when you do, remember to write from the heart. Be truthful. Tell all those people out there how you feel, what you're going through…They'll understand and support you. They already know that you and Dawn won't let them down and the farm will be reopened again as soon as it's safe to do so. Go and try to get a good night's sleep." Liza's support for us during those trying times was incredible.

For once in my life, I did as I was told and headed up to bed.

Well, after sipping at an extra large glass of Glenfiddich.

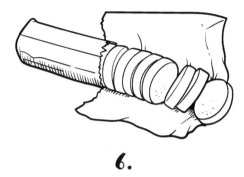

6.

The mist was hanging across the twenty-acre field as I walked slowly to the back gate. Pearl, our large shire horse, was ready to come in for her breakfast. She was leaning her weight over the top rail, almost buckling it.

I had to stretch as far as my arms could go to put the leather head collar over her head. As was often the way lately, my thoughts were miles away, unable to tear themselves away from the financial black hole we were in. And those concerns stretched all the way to Pearl. As my hands worked, my mind was considering what would happen to this gentle giant if we had to give up the farm. For some reason, I started to tell her what I was thinking.

"I'm sorry, old girl, but we're going to have to find a new home for you. Hopefully, there will be someone who will look after you and pay all your vet bills, and give you your daily Extra Strong Mint," I said to her. "It really looks as though we are finished. But, I promise you this, I will find someone to look after you."

Whilst using her 950kg body weight to push her way through the gate, she suddenly stopped and nudged at my overalls, demanding the mint that was concealed in my pocket. That seemed a fair exchange for having to listen to my troubles.

We slowly walked the short distance up the track to the stable block where she lowered her head on to my shoulder and snorted into my ear. The smell of the grass mixed with the mint she had just eaten lingered in the still early morning air. Once in the stable, she stayed still as I slipped the head collar off her head and, instead of rushing to her food trough, she stood with her head bowed towards me. It was as if this amazing animal sensed that there was a problem and, with her head over the gate, wished to share some of her wisdom with me for a few minutes more.

Even with Hollie and Charis lending a hand, there was still an awful amount of physical labour to be done, each and every day.

Having just dug out the duck houses and swept their pond, I was now fighting to push a wheelbarrow piled high with chicken manure. My legs and arms were aching so much that I was struggling to get it up the yard. Every limb in my body seemed to be locked.

Unsurprisingly, though, my thoughts were not on what I was doing at the time, despite the grief it was giving me. I had bigger problems.

I needed to approach the bank to request a larger overdraft now that the £20,000 allowance had been eaten into, and I was totally wrapped up in what I was going to say. As you might imagine, there was a lot riding on the outcome, and, even then, our problems wouldn't be solved. Having been told that we were not eligible for any Government funding, I could fully understand how mental and physical exhaustion could lead to depression; my body was shaking and my eyes watering; the negative thoughts had taken over any positive thinking that I had left in me.

Was this the start of a nervous breakdown, I was continuously asking myself.

I avoided going back into the house for my morning cup of tea until I had the chance to compose myself. In all my 68 years of living on this planet, never had I felt so low.

As I walked through the utility door, Dawn caught sight of my face.

"Are you okay?" was the simple enquiry, very quickly followed by, "I'll make a cup of tea."

We settled at the kitchen table and discussed what was the best way to proceed. Dawn managed to put another perspective on the situation.

"Why don't you set up one of these fundraising accounts to help pay for the animal feed and bedding? You know that a lot of people have been suggesting that," she said, measuring her words, knowing full well how I might respond. Which, of course, I did.

"People won't want to part with their money during these very uncertain times," I snapped. "A lot of people are out of work, others not knowing if they have a job to go back to. Come on, that simply won't work. Do you really know how much it costs to feed these animals?" My voice was now raised and angered.

Dawn, however, remained calm. "It's worth a try. We have nothing to lose and there are some very kind people out there. Why don't you give Liza a ring. I'm sure that she will help to find a way of doing it."

Her reasonableness got through to me. "Okay," I reluctantly replied. "I'll give it some thought. But I can't escape the feeling that this seems as if we're begging."

Dawn had the last say. "People will only support this if they want to."

Alan, who we get some of our calves from, called to confirm that he would remove all of the calves that we were feeding. This was a great relief. Not only were the calves time-consuming, but their feed and bedding cost was at least £25 a day. It was with mixed feelings that I had to see them go, but I consoled myself that the calves would be heading to other local farms and, eventually, would be out grazing in the New Forest.

But there was still much to do to address the animal costs. To help reduce our food bill, we had started to cut the grass in the picnic area and feed it to the Kunekune pigs. Not as simple a task as it sounds because it still meant that somebody had to cut the grass in the first place. Or, at least, that was the plan.

"I really don't know what has happened. The mower's not cutting the grass. And there's lots of smoke coming from underneath. Not sure if it's something that I've done," Charis said in her normal calm manner.

I had a look and found compacted grass wrapped around the mower's blades. "Did you not notice that the engine was struggling?" I questioned Charis as I began to pull clumps free.

"Oh, it did cut out a couple of times, but I thought that it was just my driving," she wittily replied.

The pigs were eagerly waiting at the gate by the time we got the grass to the yard, but it didn't last long. Their hungry mouths happily demolished the juicy fresh dinner in a matter of minutes.

The farm was now feeling very empty with no children playing in the outdoor play area, and no one collecting the eggs from the chicken houses. This had become another job for me. While I placed the eggs into the wire basket,

I counted them to work out if the income from the sale of these eggs would cover the cost of the feed that the chickens consumed. This was now my way of thinking; each animal had to pay their way or prove they were needed – if and when we reopened.

It was time to talk to Stuart, our accountant, again. Before the phone call, I listed a number of questions that had been bugging me for a while. It took me a while to build up the courage to discuss these things with him as I truly believed that he was going to advise me to pull the plug.

Should we stop paying all the invoices, like we had been advised?

Would we be able to increase the business overdraft?

What about the large VAT payment, which was overdue?

Could we claim for any other Government support besides the furlough arrangements?

Should we consider a fundraising page and, if so, how would we go about setting it up?

So many big questions and with one easy answer. Close the farm.

So, it was with some surprise that I found myself listening to Stuart's calm sympathetic voice. "Look, Bryan, none of this is your fault. The whole country is in this together – we just have to work out a solution. It can and will be done. Yes, of course it's going to be tough, but there's a path through this."

I could sense some optimism in his words that I hadn't felt for a long time. I couldn't get my hopes up, though.

Stuart continued: "The HMRC has already confirmed that you will not have to pay your VAT until a later date. You are an established and respected business, so your suppliers trust you, they know that you will pay your debts at some point. As for your season ticket holders, well, they'll come back, along with the school groups and everyone else. Of course, it looks pretty dire now, but you will pull through."

So, some good news and some advice on how to proceed. I asked Stuart about creating a fundraising page, half expecting to be knocked back.

"Bryan, a few weeks ago I would have told you not to bother wasting your time in setting up a fundraising page," he said. "But now? Now, I'm saying go for it. What do you have to lose. But before you consider that, you had better put together some budgets for the next three years. I'm going to set up an application for the Business Interruption Loan."

By the time I put the phone down I was, for the first time in a long time, feeling positive. We weren't out of the woods, by any measure, but there were some nuggets of hope in that phone call that gave me reason to keep trying.

I spent the rest of the morning drafting out a letter to all our suppliers that we had invoices outstanding with. I stated, plain and simply, that we were currently not in a position to pay their invoices. This was very difficult as most of our suppliers had become close friends to us and I knew some of them were struggling, too. I couldn't leave it there, though. To prove that we were honourable, I told them that we would pay 10% of the total invoice monthly until things improved.

I now had reason to believe that we should at least be able to stretch to that.

7.

I took a call from Jack the butcher who wanted to know if there were any animals he could purchase for the meat trade. Very reluctantly, I agreed to sell some of our Kunekune pigs.

"There are about forty stores here," I explained. "I'm afraid they're not up to pork weight as yet but would be ideal for sausagemeat." I felt that I was letting these small pigs down; as a farmer, I shouldn't feel like this, surely?

Abbie's little calf, now known as Renyard, was getting so large that we decided he needed more space. It was decided to give him one of the duckling runs where he had a house he could get into and, during the day, he could be out in the sun.

This little character had become humanised and Hollie can take the blame for that entirely! He had learnt that when he rubbed against the latch to the gate, it opened, so every so often he decided to take a walk around the farm. He'd tease all the other animals as he trotted around the barns, blaring at the goats and alpacas. When I tried to catch him, he would kick his feet in the air and swish his scraggy tail. I don't mind admitting that, on more than one occasion, I threatened him with my dinner plate.

When Jack arrived to collect twenty young stores, we had to be mindful of what had put us into lockdown in the first place. To reduce the risk of Covid, we had decided that we did not want to have any Longdown people nearby, so we arranged the collection and loading of the Kunekunes to be in the bottom yard, in a pen we had made up of galvanised hurdles. That way, Jack could load them up himself with his own helpers.

Unfortunately, the helpers that he had with him were not used to loading strong, lively store pigs; they stood at the tailboard of the trailer and expected the pigs to walk up the ramp. The kunes may look cute but they are certainly not silly, and they knew how to use their 30kg of body weight. They pushed their way through the makeshift hurdles and ran up the yard. Luckily, Charis and Hollie could be called upon to herd them back to the holding pen. With Jack's helpers stepping safely aside, Charis, Hollie and I took over the loading. One by one, we managed to lift them on to the clean straw bed on the trailer – but their squeals made it sound as though we were murdering them.

"Hang on a minute," I shouted, "I'm sure there were 20 pigs in here this morning but I've only counted 19 now."

"Guess you miscounted, Bryan," Hollie quickly responded. "The missing one must be under that straw in the trailer." She quickly lifted up the heavy ramp on the trailer while I worked out a sensible way of passing the movement documents over to the driver. Once done, we watched as they drove off down the road.

However, as we returned to the barn, the girls were laughing. "What's so funny?" I enquired.

"Look what Jess has found under the straw bales," Charis excitedly said.

There was a Kunekune there.

"Look, it's Babe, our favourite pig," Hollie said innocently. "She must have hidden in the straw bales. I wonder how she got in there?"

"I know how! You do realise that she's not staying. She'll have to go next time," I firmly said.

As I was finishing the feeding of the calves and washing the buckets, my phone started to ping. It was Barry, a colleague of mine: "You need to cancel your standing order to New Forest District Council immediately. The Government has just announced that they are offering all businesses like yours a payment holiday."

"What does that mean?" I cautiously asked.

"That means, Bryan, that you won't have to pay your business rates until further notice. In plain English, that will save you £43,000 a year. Now, stop whatever else you're doing and go and cancel your standing order now, otherwise you'll find it difficult to get the council to refund it." His voice had now became demanding, which is unlike Barry, but he really had a point.

I managed to cancel the standing order and email New Forest District Council as soon as I got back in. A feeling of relief washed over me as I stared at the £4500 a month standing order, now showing as cancelled on the banking screen. That would be enough to feed all the animals for another two weeks.

The National Farm Attraction Group (NFAN) had organised a Zoom meeting where all its members could virtually meet to discuss how this lockdown was going to affect us all. I had a phone call from NFAN secretary Anita, saying I should be online at 7pm on Wednesday.

"But how do I get online and talk to everyone? This is all new to me," I asked Anita.

"It's easy, Bryan. Just download the Zoom app and set the camera up and I will guide you through the rest on the night. Make sure you fit the camera on to your computer – it will give you a better quality picture," she reassuringly said.

"Okay, I'll give it a try. But I haven't got Liz in the office to help me." I feared that this may all be beyond me.

I fumbled through the Apps Store and was pleasantly surprised at how quickly I managed to download the Zoom app. Skipping through the pages of legal agreements – "Whoever reads through this lot," I asked out loud – I felt quite proud as the Zoom logo appeared on the screen. It was prompting me to install the camera.

"Ah, I know that's already installed as I used that on Facetime a few years ago." With the call to Anita finished, I was speaking to myself now. The prompt came up again, but I was getting nowhere. I was now in need of technical advice.

I called our son Aaron and explained the situation. "Firstly, Dad, do you have a camera on your computer?" he checked.

"Okay, I may be old but I'm not silly. Yes, we had one on the monitor when we spoke to Nina in Australia about a year ago," I confidently replied.

"Then there must be a wire or connection loose," he patiently replied, "so you'll need to get under the desk and try to trace the cable. Hopefully that will sort it."

Crawling under the office desk amongst a mass of different coloured cables is not a favourite pastime of mine. I spent half an hour trying to locate different leads, some heading to the printer, others to the security system, and pretending I knew what I was doing.

Dawn's welcome voice called "Fancy a cup of tea?" and I shot up from the floor like a goat kid chasing a bottle of milk. Dawn took one look at the mess I was in and said, "Why don't you call Liz? She'll most likely know how to access the camera. I'm sure she wouldn't mind you calling." Once again, Dawn's words of wisdom provided the answer.

"Liz, how do I get the camera to work on the computer? I've moved all the wires and tried the connections but it's still telling me to install the camera." I must have sounded desperate.

"Bryan, we changed the monitor about a year ago and you told me not to get one with a camera installed because you didn't like Facetime and you would never use a camera again," she very discreetly told me.

"Oh, I do remember now," I sheepishly admitted.

I needed to return to tech support.

"Aaron, where can I get a camera for my computer? I need it by Wednesday night," I asked, as casually as I could manage, hoping that he wouldn't ask too many questions.

"You silly old farmer! Are you telling me that, after all this, you don't actually have a camera on your screen after all? You plonker!" I didn't expect a sympathetic response from my son, and it appeared that I wasn't going to get one. "You'd best go on Amazon and purchase one. I'll send you a link of the better quality types as you're going to need a clear picture. There's every chance that you're going to be using it a lot. Believe me, this Covid business is not going away in a hurry!" I was very grateful for his help.

I must admit that I am not a fan of the Amazon marketplace as it seems to be taking business away from the small retailers. However, I cannot deny that their business model is simply incredible. I placed the order for the camera at 9pm and it was delivered at 9am the next morning. Once again, I called Aaron to seek more advice.

"Where do I plug this camera into?" I began, but he cut me off.

"You get yourself out of the office now and I'll come up and fit it in for you. But, remember, you and mum must not be in the office; we must keep our distance. And make sure you spray the desk and keyboard with an antiseptic spray before I get there, please."

•

When the office door opened, I heard the sound of a young child's voice.

"Where's Nana? I want to see her." This was Evie, our granddaughter, who was standing outside the office door, trying to get a glimpse of her Nana and Granddad.

Aaron very sternly said: "Shh, you aren't meant to be here. You mustn't go inside the office. Nana will speak through the window."

How do you explain to a four-year-old child that she cannot give her Nana a hug or kiss. Now, I'm not a cuddly person so it didn't affect me so much, but Nana and Evie carried on blowing kisses through the window as Aaron installed the new camera on to the computer.

"There you go, Dad," called Aaron. "It's all ready to go. We could try it out later this evening and have a family Zoom call." He persuaded Evie to come away from the window, making it very clear that there were not to be any hugs or kisses, just a wave through the glass-fronted door. "Nana and Granddad mustn't get the germs as they may die," he somewhat cruelly said. "Now, we don't want that to happen, do we?"

Evie's face looked sad as she always liked to hug and kiss her Nana. But if she couldn't touch, she could certainly ask questions. "Nana, how long before I can come into your house and play with my toys? I really want to sleep in my bed in your house. Can I see Jess? I really miss her. When will these germs go away and when will I be able to come to the farm again? I miss seeing all the animals."

It was interesting to see the situation through Evie's eyes. How could a four-year-old ever understand why all these restrictions were in place?

My mind swung back to the computer with its newly fitted camera. "Before you disappear, er, how do I use it?" It seemed sensible to get all the help I could while Aaron was here, although actually being able to see while maintaining our distance wasn't at all easy. I settled for standing outside the door.

"Now, do not touch any of those wires and when you link on to the Zoom call, just press that button there," Aaron explained. "Don't forget to press the mute symbol otherwise everyone will be able to hear the dogs barking. And, before you use the keyboard, ensure you sterilise it with the spray," he lectured me in his normal bossy way. Frankly, I was quite happy to be lectured.

"I thought that we were a family bubble and that we could see Aaron, Lou and little Evie?" Dawn questioned me afterwards.

"Well, it hasn't been confirmed by the Government what a family bubble is," I replied. "I know that Kerry and Charley are definitely in our bubble as they are required to work here, but Aaron doesn't want us to mix at the moment because of the high risk, which I fully understand. Guess we just need to be patient and hopefully it will sort itself out very quickly." I did my best to explain but, judging by the body language aimed at me, it was not the answer that Dawn was looking for.

8.

It seemed so strange as I walked around the farm with Jess close to my side. Normally, at this time of day, children would be racing down the yard, eager to pick up the freshly laid eggs. The play area was deserted and the silence felt eerie. The only sounds that I could hear were the very noisy goats eagerly waiting for their milk. I was convinced that the animals were missing the interaction as much as I was.

As I headed back to the farmhouse, Dawn greeted me at the door. "I've just come off the phone to one of our season ticket holders. She is adamant that we should set up a GoFundMe page. Isn't that what you were talking about?" Dawn enquired.

"Yes, it's all in hand. Hopefully we'll put the appeal out later this week," I abruptly responded. In truth, I wasn't even sure how it all worked, let alone how to start an appeal. It was another enormous unknown amongst weeks of enormous unknowns. It just wasn't something I could get my mind around.

Sat in the office once more, I found myself trawling through all the possible grants and financial aid on offer to help us get through this difficult time. Our costs continued to far outweigh the negligible amount coming in, and that would only get worse day by day. I needed to find a solution, or series of solutions, to plug the gap in our finances. It seemed more and more apparent that – despite all the positive vibes the Government was putting out – we were not eligible for most of the handouts that were on offer. It was hugely frustrating.

I slumped into the chair and continued to scroll through these pages, hoping that something would crop up.

Increasingly, an appeal of some sort was looking more and more likely.

•

Liza, our publicity manager, and I had agreed to conduct all our meetings over the phone. "That suits me fine; it means that you won't be able to see my fading roots," Liza jokingly said. "Right, we need to discuss this fundraising page idea."

All this was new to both of us. "Where do we start?" I asked.

"Firstly, you'll need to make a video to explain to our season ticket holders why we require help," Liza proposed.

"You can forget that," I abruptly interrupted her. "There's no way that I'm going to stand in front of a camera, begging for money. I don't mind writing it in a newsletter but no way am I going to embarrass myself by blabbering on a video!"

Liza calmly disagreed with me. "You'll be able to do this. You've always been good at speaking from your heart. All the people that know you will listen to what you have to say and will support you. Believe me, you're not begging. It's not your fault that you've found yourself in this situation. There are a lot of people out there who simply love Longdown and all that it has provided over the years. Think of the joy it's brought to so many families, and all the students that you have given an opening to their future careers. Believe me, Bryan, you really do need to make a video of this. I know it won't be easy, but you can do it, I promise."

Reluctantly, I agreed to give it a try. "I'll try to video myself on my phone," I begrudgingly replied, "but I make no promises."

While I was shutting the poultry away, as the sun went down, my mind was rehearsing what I needed to say on this video. I was not comfortable about it at all.

I wandered into the peaceful picnic area and parked myself on a bench, pulling my mobile phone and some notes from my pocket. Jess jumped up alongside me, as if to give morale support. I really wasn't ready for this.

Holding the phone up, I fumbled with the record button and started to speak. Only then did I realise that I was filming the outdoor play area. I hadn't flipped the camera.

"This is bloody stupid," I blared out to Jess. She just wagged her tail and nudged into me as though to say "have another try".

I tried to speak my well-rehearsed words, but it became more and more difficult to the point that I threw the phone to the ground in a fit of rage as all the frustration and unfairness of the situation boiled over.

"How did it go?" Dawn enquired as I went back into the house.

"It didn't," I sharply responded. "There's no way that I'll be able to do it. It's a stupid idea!"

"Why don't you try tomorrow? Simply throw the notes away and just speak as though you're talking to a group of children; you're good at that. That way, there'll be less pressure on you," Dawn calmly said.

I wasn't convinced.

I spent the rest of the evening Googling all the activity farms that I knew of and checking if any of them had put out an appeal, and if any of them had put out supporting videos. I found a few and watched them over and over again; some appeared to be very professional at being in front of the camera while others were just like me – true novices!

I watched Doug Douglas from Avon Valley Country Park, and his video gave me the inspiration to just get up there and tell it as it was. Doug passionately told his audience that their farm park was going to have to close as they as a family could no longer sustain it during the present lockdown. Because I knew Doug, his words chimed with me both on a personal and professional level; he would only do this if he was desperate. He was fighting the same battle for survival that we were.

"Sorry it's late, Liza, but I thought that I'd call to let you know that I failed to film the video tonight," I said. I may not have been feeling confident, but I was certainly feeling inspired. "I promise that I'll get it done tomorrow."

"No worries," was her simple response. "Try with a refreshed mind and it'll be easier. Good luck."

I'd committed myself. I'd film something, whatever that may be, the next day.

Pearl really does not like taking her wormer. As both Hollie and I tried to persuade her to swallow the large tablet, we tried disguising it in a carrot, which she quickly spat out. Then, we held her head down and tried to slip it into the back of her mouth while we held her rubbery lips open. In return, she simply lifted her head higher and higher, despite us being on tiptoes, casually reaching a height that left us no choice but to let go. That's when you realise just how tall and magnificent these gentle giants are.

Knowing just how much she enjoys an Extra Strong Mint, I managed to crush the tablet into a bucket along with the tasty treat. When offered, she scoffed it down within seconds.

Hollie had been considering the Shire throughout all this. "Who will take on Pearl, with her sleeping disorder and all her other veterinary requirements, if we have to find a new home for her? Surely no one will want to take her on? Will it mean you'll have to put her to sleep?" She hid her face in Pearl's long mane; this was the first time that I'd witnessed Hollie accepting that we were close to closure.

"Now, come on, we're not giving up yet. We'll work something out," I promised. "I'm going to make this video tonight and see if we get any response from that. And, if that doesn't work, I'll find another way. So stop thinking negative. We have to work together on this. Come on, let's get these animals out into the field."

Hollie moved her head from Pearl's mane and managed a weak smile, trying to hide her puffed eyes as she slowly lead her best friend down the track into the field.

"Charley, you're good with your phone. Can you help me make a video?" I was interrupting her while she was sat in our dining room doing her school work. Well, pretending to.

"I'm too busy with my project to help now, maybe later this afternoon," she said, distractedly.

I guess this was the response that I was expecting from my nearly fourteen-year-old granddaughter, although I was disappointed. "Project? I've listened to you chatting to your friends for at least half an hour and, if you call that school work, I'd better have a word with your teacher," I angrily responded.

What I hadn't realised was that she had her phone on loud speaker and all her friends had witnessed my outrage, which caused them to giggle. This just annoyed me even more.

"Forget it! I'll ask someone else," I snapped as I slammed the office door. Maybe I was being a bit harsh as it's not very often that Charley and I clash.

The thought of making this video was taking its toll.

Jess ran around to the duck area and waited patiently at the gate. "Come on," I called. "Let's make this video before the sun moves over. We'll shut the poultry away a bit later."

As though this intelligent dog knew what I'd said, she raced to the picnic bench by the classroom and perched herself on top, almost beckoning me to sit down. Once again, I pulled my mobile phone from my pocket and sat next to my faithful dog. "Right, let's get this done."

She wagged her tail and pushed her nose on to my hand as though to say "get on with it".

I cleared my throat and ran my fingers through my messy mop of hair in an attempt to tidy it up. The missed haircut was now showing.

Taking care to aim the camera directly at my face, with the correct camera selected, I pressed the video icon. Now all I had to do was to start speaking.

Amazingly, the words came. Slowly at first, they began to pour out of my mouth more confidently than I had expected as I fumbled through the things that had to be said. I was well aware that I needed to make this sincere and ensure that the listeners understood that we were in desperate need of help to feed the animals. And all in the 120 seconds that Liza had advised me to limit it to.

My throat was becoming dry and my voice was showing signs of emotion as the last words rolled out. By the time my finger glided over the stop icon, there was a feeling of relief that it was all over. What I couldn't know was whether it was any good. Regardless, I was feeling positive.

Jess appeared more excited than me as we headed off to shut the poultry away. Passing the stables, Chesney – our cheeky Shetland pony – rushed to the fence to take the Extra Strong Mint from my hand; this is his nightly treat which he has become accustomed to.

With the jobs finally done, we went back into the house and I passed the phone to Dawn. "Well, I've done it," was all I said as I walked past her.

"Well done. Can I look?" she replied, watching every move of my facial expressions.

"Yes, but be truthful. If you don't like it, tell me. I really don't want to make a fool of myself," was my response as I headed to the kitchen to make a cup of tea.

As the kettle boiled, Dawn came up to me, grinning. "Bryan, that's perfect! Right to the point and very emotional. It certainly doesn't sound as though you're begging and you're just saying it as it is. Well done." This was a relief to hear, make no mistake. As always, her encouraging words gave me a boost. "Just one thing, though: you really should have combed your hair before videoing it!"

"Well, that's it, then, I'll send it over to Liza and see what she thinks," I said. "One thing's for sure, I am not doing it again if she doesn't like it! We'll forget about the whole thing!" The tone of my voice betrayed my mixed feelings of aggravation and relief.

Within minutes of me sending the video across to Liza, my mobile rang. Before I answered it, I said to Dawn: "Well, this is it: the final decision is about to be revealed."

"Oh, Bryan, that's so wonderful; full of passion and emotion. I had to find a box of tissues for my eyes," Liza enthused. "You've got the point over so well. I knew you could do it. Well done, you! I'll get that out there tomorrow!" She sounded excited. In truth, I was feeling a bit of that, too.

9.

With the recent rainfall, I decided today would be ideal to roll the sixteen-acre field at the back of the farm. Having topped up the International tractor with diesel, I hitched the large rollers to the draw bar and headed across the very bumpy field with the clatter of the metal roller bouncing up and down. Its job was to press the stones and soil down in an attempt to level the field up a little.

With the radio blasting out some weird funky music, I used this as useful thinking time for me to ponder the things I could put into the newsletter. This was the brainchild of Liza who had persuaded me to write on a weekly basis at our last phone-meeting.

"What on earth will I write about?" I'd said. "Surely people will get bored of hearing about the struggles that we're going through and, quite truthfully, I'm feeling so downhearted that it will just sound depressing." I was working hard to convince her otherwise.

"Bryan, you have the ability to put a positive slant on even the worst situation," she said, batting by objections back at me. "You have passion in what you do and your visitors will be interested in how you and Dawn are coping during these dreadful times. I know it's more work for you but I promise it will be well worth the effort. Go on, give it a try. It's only for a few weeks, surely."

I agreed, and, once again, realised I'd been pushed into something which was out of my comfort zone.

And so there I was, rolling around the field, thinking about a newsletter. With the appeal video made and in Liza's lap, my mind was now elsewhere.

Not that I ever have long to concentrate on any one thing. There are always several tasks fighting for my attention, and they often involve an animal.

So it was that day, when I later found myself dealing with Blossom. She was standing very patiently as we held her against the stable wall; well, that was until Hollie touched the abscess on the foot of the white alpaca. Without any warning, Blossom turned her head, made a piercing shrill noise, then spat the full contents of the partially digested grass into our faces. As we scrabbled to move away, she seemed to take great delight in regurgitating another mouthful to follow up on the first.

This normally timid and shy creature had turned into an aggressive, dangerous animal.

"I think you hurt her," I said to Hollie as we cleaned the slimy grass off our faces. Hollie was now in hysterics.

"Look at the state of me! We'll just have to catch her again to inject the antibiotics into her muscle. What weight do you think she is?" Hollie enquired as she drew the penicillin from the glass bottle.

"I would guess about 75 kilograms," I responded, weighing her up instantly with my years of experience.

Blossom had now quietened down. We cornered her and were soon slowly injecting the white substance of long acting penicillin into her leg muscle.

"She needs to be out in the field with the others," I suggested, knowing there would be objections to my suggestion.

"It's far too wet and muddy out there and how will we catch her if we need to treat her again," was the response I'd anticipated.

"Sorry, she needs to be outside. Leaving her in the stables will not help her; she needs to be out with the others. We'll be able to bring them all in if we need to treat her, so let's put her out now," I said, showing a little authority.

When we opened the field gates, Blossom raced towards the others. They danced around in the long grass, so excited to see each other. Blossom had already forgotten about the abscess on her foot.

"I'm trying to find my way around this GoFundMe page; it's so complicated," Liza informed me on our call a little later.

"I know, I had a look myself last night and gave up. Should we just forget about it?" I must have sounded defeated.

"Oh, no. You've made the video, so we must continue! I'll call you later

today; there has to be a way around this," Liza confidently advised me.

"Please don't set it up yet," I added. "I'm on a Zoom meeting with the National Farm Attraction Group later this evening and I'll ask how other farms have managed this. Maybe it's not such a good idea." But my response was falling on deaf ears.

"We'll get this out there ASAP. You and the animals need this and this is your only chance, Bryan." I could hear frustration in Liza's voice as she sensed me wavering. "Swallow your pride, just this once, and ask for help. It's nothing to be ashamed of."

"Okay, but let's at least find out what the other group members say and I'll get back to you this evening," I sheepishly suggested.

"It will all be set up, waiting for me to press the button to make it live," was the confident response.

Before Covid, I had never heard of a Zoom meeting before. And yet, here I was now, facing a group of 125 like-minded farm attraction owners and managers. I couldn't help but scroll through the attendees to see if I recognised any of the other delegates.

"Hi, Charlie, it's good to see you," I was shouting at the screen.

"Bryan, you should be on mute," warned Tom, who was chairing the meeting. It then seemed as if the entire 125 members tried to explain where I would find the elusive mute button.

As the meeting progressed, I found myself getting involved. I was relaxing into it and managing to press the correct button to mute and unmute myself – until I didn't. Somehow I had hit the share button.

"Bryan, you're sharing your emails to all of us! Please get them off," Tom shouted. I did my best to hastily comply, well aware that everyone was watching.

It was now or never so I plucked up the courage to ask a question of my own. "Can anyone tell me if they have put out an appeal to feed their animals and, if so, was it successful? Does anybody have any tips on how to do this?"

Doug Douglas was quick to respond. "Yes, it's worth doing if you wish to raise two or three thousand pounds," he said, but the general opinion seemed to be that it wasn't worth all the hassle. This was, to say the least, disheartening.

After we all waved goodbye at the end of the meeting, I phoned Liza with the news. "I'm not sure if it's worth it, judging what the others are saying."

"They aren't you, or Longdown. You have a different customer base than all the other attractions; the families and schools that visit you simply love Longdown and feel part of the family. I'm truly confident they'll help you," Liza insisted. "I'm pressing the button now, and I'm ready to promote it on social media and the season ticket mailing list."

It seemed that Liza had taken control.

Well, I guess that's what we pay her for.

10.

"Well, that's it. Liza has put the appeal out," I said to Dawn as I pulled on my boots. "I'm shutting the poultry away and checking on the horses. While I'm out there I might as well take the dogs across the field to check on Abbie."

But I knew that trying to make conversation with Dawn whilst Emmerdale was on was practically impossible. Jess jumped up from her bed and headed to the door; this was the time of day that she loved the most.

Climbing over the fences to reach the duck pens had become a harder task for my aching limbs, as had crouching through the fallen branches to catch one particular chicken that had decided it wanted to stay out for the night. "Come on, young lady, no use you sitting out here. That fox will soon be on his rounds and will have you for his tea!"

Yes, I was talking to the animals once again, which may be a first sign of madness but at least they don't answer back. All the time this was going on my phone was vibrating continuously in my pocket but I was ignoring it. Instead, my thoughts were on the appeal that had now gone out. Had I made a fool of myself? I pictured it circulating through social media and on to people's phones and computers; me babbling, begging, looking a scruffy emotional wreck. I was really regretting that I'd let myself get talked into 'pressing the button'.

Jess nuzzled into me as we sat on the picnic bench, watching the herd of fallow deer playing in the field below while my mind drifted, turning it all over again and again. "Wow, look at the time, Jess. We'd better get back in."

Dawn knew that I needed some quiet time and didn't question me as to why I had been so long as I headed to the front room. "Kerry and Aaron have been trying to get hold of you. They say that your appeal has gone out on Facebook. Apparently there are a lot of people donating already."

"I'll have a look in the morning," I replied. "I feel completely knackered now."

Dawn shook her head. "You'd better call them now. They seem very excited and were wondering why you weren't answering your phone. I think they're worried about you."

Before she finished speaking, my phone started to vibrate again. "If that's them then you'd better answer it," Dawn insisted.

"Dad, where on earth have you been? Your ugly mug has been shared on so many Facebook accounts, your video has gone viral!" blurted out Aaron. "Have you seen the GoFundMe page? I reckon that you'll reach the £5000 target tonight, if it continues at this rate!" His voice was a mix of emotion.

"How do I find the page to check the amount?" I asked. It hadn't even occurred to me to ask this before now.

"Simply go to the GoFundMe site, search for Longdown, and you'll see it. It's like a fruit machine, the amount is increasing all the time." I could hear him becoming agitated with me at being such a dinosaur on the computer. I told him I'd call him back.

As I sat down to turn on the iPad, Kerry phoned. "Dad, have you seen the things that people are saying about you and Mum on Facebook?"

"Oh, Christ, don't tell Mum if they are slagging us off," was my immediate response.

"No, quite different. It's as if the whole of Facebook loves you both and the farm. It's so touching." Kerry was now the emotional one. "Have a look, Dad, it's just gone crazy. I think you've reached your target already."

As I read out the comments to Dawn, my voice began to falter, so I gave her the iPad for her to read herself. "Do you realise that we've reached the target already?" I said, utterly stunned. "And – look at this – our friends and staff are donating! This is so embarrassing. Should we stop it now that we've reached the target?" I didn't have a clue what to do. "I'll call Liza and see what she says."

"What on earth have you done?" were my first words to Liza as she picked up the phone.

"I know! We're watching it now. It's wonderful, isn't it?" she replied with delight.

"Should we stop the appeal now that we've reached the target? I'm not sure how this works," I hesitantly enquired.

"God, no, people will only donate if they want to . You know as well as me that this pandemic will be here for a long time – you'll need as much support as you can get." Her words of wisdom came over forcibly so I didn't attempt to challenge her. "Bryan, I'm so happy for you all. It really does prove how much both of you and the farm are loved. You deserve it. Well done."

After the call, I sat trying to take it all in. "I can't take anymore of this; I'm off to bed. There's still lots to do tomorrow," I said, turning off the telly.

"Well, at least, for once, it's not all depressing news tonight," Dawn concluded.

It's very satisfying to go into the chicken house and collect up the eggs. At least we had some income coming in from the farm and the eggs formed a small part of that.

As I crawled over the perches to collect the ones which the chickens had laid on the floor, the very large Light Sussex hopped on to the side of the basket. We always have a chat in the morning, normally about how many eggs I've collected or sometimes about the weather. But this morning my mind was on the appeal and so I didn't pay her any attention. Frustrated with me, she puffed up her feathers and made a very large clucking noise, then shook her whole body.

The basket full of eggs went flying, breaking the majority of the fifty or so eggs that I had just collected. As I called her names that are not in the Bible, salvaging as many eggs as I could, she treated me with complete contempt by jumping into the basket, refusing to move.

"The phone's been extremely busy this morning," Dawn advised me as I walked through the door. "I've dealt with most of them but you'll need to return some calls before you go out again. Three groups have offered to donate fruit and vegetables for the animals: MCD Fruit & Veg, Totton Isolation Group, and Sam from Marchwood. I've told them that you'll call them back."

"That's kind of them," I said, "but, legally, we're not allowed to feed the animals any by-products unless we know its original source."

"That's complete rubbish," Dawn retorted. "So, what you're saying is that we should let the animals starve because of some idiotic regulation?" Dawn was annoyed that I should even consider rejecting these kind offers.

"Hold fire. I'm only quoting the legal requirement. I'm not saying that we'll turn it down. We'll take it and, if we get told off for it at a later date, we'll deal with it then," I responded defensively.

Who would have thought that trying to do the right thing would be so hard. Balancing the needs of the animals and the dire situation with the rules and regulations was just another problem to negotiate.

I decided that, with the pile of paperwork on my desk not getting any smaller, I had better spend an hour or so in the office. Charley was chatting away to friends whilst doing her school work in the dining room, next door. Somehow, I soon realised, I had managed to lock myself out of the internet banking. No matter how much I swore at the computer, it wasn't going to let me into the bank account. "Where is Liz when you need her?" I blathered, talking to myself.

"Are you okay in there, Granddad?" Charley enquired.

"This is ridiculous. What's the good of internet banking when it logs you out!" I grumbled loudly.

"Call the helpline," she responded quickly. "That's what they're there for." Good advice, I suppose, from a fourteen-year-old.

The very polite and patient adviser on the other end of the phone listened as I explained that I was a farmer and not a computer buff and I was at the end of my fuse. Very professionally, she advised me what to do. "Sit back in your seat for a while, look at the screen, and pretend that there's a field of animals on there."

"How will that get the banking back online?" I snapped.

"It won't, however it will put you in a better frame of mind and you won't be so agitated," she replied quietly. "Now, have you anything in your browser?"

"The only browsers I have are forty-odd goats," I replied a little tartly. Judging from the giggles and laughter, I believe I made her day. Moments later, I was logged back in.

"Looks as though we'll have to cancel all the school bookings because they've just announced that this bloody lockdown will need to be in place for at least another six weeks. Shall we wait for the schools to contact us or would it be best for us to contact them?" I was reluctantly seeking Dawn's opinion.

"Surely they already know as the children aren't at school. It would take hours to contact them all. And, remember, the teachers won't be there, anyway. Let's leave it for the time being," said Dawn. "We have enough on our plates."

Advice taken.

But I wasn't done. I'd had an idea and I wanted to run it past her. "I'm going to put together some educational videos and put them on Facebook, so the children can still see what happens on the farm," I told her.

"And who's going to take the videos? Have you forgotten how long it took you to film your appeal, and all the stress of it?" was Dawn's response.

"I'll ask Charley. She's good with the phone and it shouldn't take long. There are so many animals we could talk about and there could even be one about the tractor." I was now becoming really enthusiastic about my new idea. I just needed to persuade Charley, but that would have to wait. I had an appointment out in the field.

"Why on earth do cows go right to the bottom of the field to have their calves?" I was grumbling again. "Nora was by the gate just fifteen minutes ago. Now she's wandered off to the bottom of the field. I can see the calf's legs sticking out."

Understandably, I was not very impressed that I had to walk through the mud to reach her. "Why did you not wait up the top, it would have been a lot easier for both of us," I said to her whilst slipping the calving ropes over the straggly legs. One small tug and the calf dropped on to the grass below. "Another boy. Not sure what's going to happen to you," I said. I removed the mucus from its nostrils and inspected the newest member of the farm.

"And another mouth to feed," I sighed.

No two days are the same as a farmer, and that's a mixed blessing. One moment you're helping birth a calf, the next you're wrangling escapees.

"I should have got rid of these goats weeks ago," I shouted to Hollie as we struggled to get them back into their paddock. "Look, they've wrecked the electric cars. Lucky you turned the power off last week otherwise we would have electrocuted goats on our hands."

I was being completely ignored, though. Hollie was busy videoing the goats standing on the cars with the steering wheels in their mouths. "Oh, Bryan, just in case you haven't noticed, there are about twenty others in the chicken run. They've flattened the fence," Hollie said. And off she went to collect a feed bag for them to follow.

These sort of events are a good distraction from a troubled mind. I'd not thought about the farm's troubles, or the appeal, for a couple of hours by the time I returned to the farmhouse.

Straight away, Dawn warned me that a well-spoken lady had phoned earlier, insisting that she spoke to the owner. In no time at all I found myself talking to her. "Good morning, I need to speak to the man who owns this place," she said in an abrupt, no-nonsense voice. "I wish to donate some money to your animals, young man."

"Of course, that's very kind of you, madam," I politely responded.

"Can you assure me that the animals will benefit from this and not you?" Her tone was formidable.

"Yes, certainly, you have my assurance that every single penny that is raised will go towards feeding the animals at Longdown," I said pleasantly.

"Give me your address. I will send you a cheque. I do not use a computer," she informed me.

I felt very awkward following the call. Taking donations over the internet was impersonal – something that was happening at a distance. But that call had been direct and to the point. I'd never for a moment considered that that might happen.

Two days later, we received a letter with an extremely generous cheque for £1000. The accompanying message simply said 'for the animals'.

"There are some very kind people out there," I told Dawn as I checked the envelope for any clues as to who this wonderful woman could be.

"Yes, I know. Look, there's another one here from Marjorie and you had better read what she says. It's all so wonderful, and yet so embarrassing," Dawn said, passing me the letter.

I then located an email for Dawn to read. "Look, it's from that little boy who loves feeding the goats. He's told his mum that he wants his pocket money to feed the animals at Longdown."

"Who are Ted and Millie?" Dawn interrupted me. She was glancing at the donation page.

"You know who they are – that's Kevin and Pauline's dog and tortoise," I responded.

"They're so kind! But how do they know about the appeal?" she asked.

I simply shrugged my shoulders. I didn't have the answer.

11.

"I've been working on your behalf to claim for a Business Interruption Loan. It's quite complex and they do require a lot of information from you." Stuart was treading carefully as he approached the subject.

"The bank manager, Darren, hasn't even responded to my emails and phone calls, so how on earth can I give him the information required," I sharply responded.

"That's why I've taken it upon myself to sort this out for you. I know only too well that you have plenty on your plate already. All I need is your trading accounts for the past three years, which I have, then your budgets for the next three years. I'll send you the templates to assist you," he tentatively informed me. I guess it's easy for an accountant to do this sort of thing but, for me, it was a mammoth task. And I knew where I could find some help. I put in a call to Tim, the business consultant.

"Tim, not sure if you can assist but I need to work on budgets for the next few years," I explained.

"No problem at all, Bryan. I'm sat on my backside doing sod all so I'll be happy to do that for you. I'll send over a spreadsheet with some figures for you to approve and job will be done," Tim confidently, and quite brilliantly, responded.

He did exactly that, and soon I was going through the figures. Or, at least, trying.

"Bryan, what on earth is up? I can hear you shouting from upstairs." Dawn looked worried as she came into the office. "Look, it's gone two o'clock."

My face, I suspected, said it all. "I've just spent hours entering all this information on this spreadsheet and then I've pressed this button here and it's wiped off all the details that I entered!" My frustration and anger was echoing through the tone of my voice.

"You're tired. Just leave it tonight and, maybe, if you call Liz tomorrow, she can help," she said and went back to bed.

I acknowledged defeat and followed her.

The side of the garden had become overgrown and I knew this irritated Dawn more than anything. It was time to get out the strimmer and clear the area.

Armed with goggles and gloves, I entered the small paddock, knowing this was going to be a colossal task. However, before I reached the weeds, Dawn was beckoning me over whilst holding a tray of coffee cups and biscuits.

"Why don't you put the geese into this area; they'd love it out here and it will be nice to have them close to the house."

"That's a great idea," I had to admit. "And they've started laying so I can get my breakfast in return."

I was happy with this plan.

By now, like much of the country, we'd settled into the routine that lockdown had presented us. Although there was plenty of scope for things to get worse, we were making the best of a bad situation. Our finances were still incredibly bleak, but the appeal had bought us some time. And then, in late May, there was a glimmer of hope regarding lockdown.

"Did you hear the news this morning, Dad? It sounds as though the Government are considering removing all the lockdown restrictions. It even looks like the open spaces will be one of the first to allow visitors again. Surely that's fantastic news?" Kerry seemed to have more confidence in what the media reported than me.

"Just don't get too excited," I replied pessimistically. "Did you hear that the cases in Southampton and the New Forest have risen dramatically? And we may not be classified as an open space because of the contact our visitors have with the animals. Personally, I believe we'll be in lockdown for a very long time yet." I noted I was looking on the negative side, which is unusual for me.

"This is ridiculous, look at all those people in the Farm Shop!" worried Dawn. "It's far too crowded. It won't be long before someone goes down with Covid."

"We can't close it as too many people rely on it to get their food. We're an essential service." I tried to sound convincing.

"It's unfair to put Richard and Wayne at such a risk. I think we ought to put them both on furlough," Kerry interrupted.

This required a discussion with Wayne.

"Wayne, what do you think?" I asked.

"I'll be honest with you: when I see all these people coming through the shop, it does worry me. There are still a lot of people not wearing masks, even though I ask them to. As long as you think you can afford it, I believe that it would be best to close it for the time being," he said with a great deal of apprehension.

"I agree entirely. Why put us all at risk?" Dawn said, nodding her head in agreement.

"Well, we might as well close down completely and go bankrupt," I said, my voice trembling. "If there's no income from the shop or the farm then that's it. I simply can't see how we can survive. We may as well pull the plug now."

"Hang on, Dad, don't get so shirty. There's a way round this: Mum and I can take orders over the phone and put them in bags ready for collection at the shop entrance. We won't be mixing with people, and we are all in the same bubble. It'll be fun. If we all work together at this, we'll be able to make it work." Kerry had taken control once again. "Wayne, we'll need you to help with the ordering, though, if you don't mind."

"No problem," he quickly replied.

Charley had become very good at filming the Little Farmers videos. "Come on, Granddad, we need to get three videos done today," she said. "It's your fault for promising all those children that you would put one out each week."

She wasn't wrong. But these videos were proving a real tonic for me to make, and were proving popular, too.

"Let's get the cows and calves, and horses, done today whilst it's dry," Charley said, bossing me around.

Abbie the cow enjoys a lot of attention and was keen to pose whilst Charley was trying to video me explaining where milk came from. I forgot that Charley is not a fan of large cows so, when Abbie decided to stand between me and Charley, edging closer to her in the middle of the video, it all ended abruptly in screaming. All I saw was this lanky body running across the field.

It looked like I'd lost my camera operator.

"Tim and Ed have arrived," said Charis over the radio. For a moment there I'd forgotten that the blacksmiths were coming.

They got straight to work on Pearl who immediately got up to her usual tricks as she lashed out with her 950kg weight as the boys tried to trim her overgrown hooves.

By the time I reached the stable block, they had bribed her with a block of garlic lick. This appeared to keep her occupied while they used the large clippers to cut back the surplus hoof. Jess was waiting in anticipation, eventually rewarded when Tim threw a chunk of the white horn in her direction.

"Looks as though Ed's drawn the short straw," I laughed as Charis held on for dear life. Amber, the Mediterranean donkey, reared up, refusing to let Ed near her. "It's always the smaller ones that give all the grief," said Ed as he attempted to pull her back to the side of the stable.

Once the blacksmiths were done, I headed back to the office – there was always paperwork that needed doing.

"This same number has called several times today but when I answer the phone there's no one there," Dawn said as I went inside. "I've written it down just in case you know who it is."

"That's young Joe's. I recognise that number. I'll give him a call," I said as I punched the number into the phone. "Good morning, Farmer Joe, how are you doing?"

"Oh, great, Farmer Bryan. How are all the cows and the goats? What about the geese and horses? I love reading your newsletters," he said, all in an excited tumble.

Joe had been a regular visitor to the farm since he was a small boy and it was very difficult for him – and many other children and adults with learning difficulties – to understand why they couldn't visit the farm at the moment. Judging from the excited tone of his voice, I guessed these few minutes had made his day, especially when I told him that I'd call again next week.

This gave me another idea. I sought out Hollie and Charis. "I have a list of some of the students who are unable to come to the farm and I feel it would be a good idea if we could call them once a week just to keep them involved in what's happening," I explained.

"That would be good," Hollie agreed. "I'll call Romana. Charis, you have Henry. And, Bryan, you can speak to Caitlin. And good luck with that as you'll never get off the phone," she giggled.

"Farmers and technology simply don't go together, do they?" Tim was in hysterics as I was explaining what had happened to my budget figures on the computer. "But no need to worry about it. Before you managed to wipe it off, you had somehow managed to send me a copy, so, if you don't mind, I'll deal with Stuart directly. Guess it'll be safer that way. You get back outside and feed all the animals; that's what you're good at." I was taking the ribbing on the chin. It seemed only fair, what with all the help Tim was giving me. Still chuckling loudly, he added, "Bryan, you and Dawn must be the most popular people in Hampshire. I've been following your GoFundMe appeal. It's just amazing! Over £34,000 and still rising. You must be so pleased."

I was only too aware. It had put us all in a constant state of amazement. "We are but we're also embarrassed that it's gone so well," I confessed. "Although, it does look as though we'll need every single penny of it." My voice was now becoming very emotional.

"Most people have to die before their obituary is printed but, in your case, looking on Facebook and the GoFundMe page, there are thousands of comments reflecting on the impact you've had on people. You two have such a following. They won't let you close down. Well done, the pair of you. It's very well deserved. Now, let's get on with the business of getting you the Business Interruption Loan. With all the support you're receiving, surely the bank won't dare turn you down." As usual, Tim's reassuring words brightened up my spirits.

But all that changed later that day when Dawn took a call from Wayne, the Farm Shop manager.

"Wayne has just called to say that he's gone down with Covid and both him and Lisa are very poorly," Dawn explained. "They haven't been able to get out of bed and Wayne said that his legs are feeling like lumps of steel. I asked him if he believes he caught it from someone visiting the shop but he's confident that it was Lisa who contracted it from one of the doctors at the surgery where she works. It's some consolation that the virus wasn't in the shop, but I'm really worried about him. He sounds awful."

Kerry's ears pricked up. "Oh, no! Who's going to show me the difference between a Maris Piper and a King Edward potato?" she squealed. But it wasn't going to get her down. "We really are on own out there now. And all when we've been getting all those enquiries about the food boxes we've advertised. I'm sure we'll soon find our way with all the different fruits and vegetables," she added confidently.

"Let's hope Rich is all clear. I'll send him a text," I chipped in.

12.

"It's time to think a bit positive." Kerry came into the kitchen as we were munching on our breakfast. "There's talk of retail outlets being able to open. Does that mean that people will be able to come inside the shop again or will we need to continue the click and collect scheme as we are doing?"

"It's all a bit too complicated at the moment and I'm sure that Wayne and Rich will be happier to stay on furlough rather than take the risk of mixing with people again," Dawn joined in.

"Well, I am concerned that if we don't open fully soon, you two are going to wear yourselves out," I said. "We ought to work on a plan on how we can open. We all know that it won't be for months yet. When we are actually able to open, we'll need to install screens around the counter and put markers two metres apart around the floor; all added expense for us, but – hey-ho – at least there's something we can work towards." I wanted to get the last word in.

And, I realised, I was being positive again.

"Anyone fancy moving all that dung in the Midden," I enquired as Hollie and Charis sipped on their cups of coffee.

"That'll be fun," Charis responded as quick as lightning. "I like a challenge."

"We need to get all of it down into the field whilst the ground is dry. Then, hopefully, we can spread it in September. Doesn't look as though we'll be buying any fertiliser this year," I said, putting a negative spin on the subject.

"What about the heap in the car park? It will be so much easier to cross the road now that there's hardly any traffic using it," Hollie suggested.

"We'll leave that for the gardeners. Guess more people will be growing their own food during the next few months. Not only that, we simply haven't got the time to move it all," I responded. Throwing my paper cup into the bin, I added: "The amount of cars on the road reminds me of what it was like when Dawn and I first moved here about 40 years ago."

"The office phone's ringing," Dawn informed me as I was heading up the stairs to bed.

"Who on earth would be calling at this time of night?" I complained. "Guess I'd better check if they left a message." I felt a shiver as the stern voice identifying himself as a police officer informed me that a heifer was causing chaos on the road outside the farm. "Could you call 101 and quote 'Cow'," he said.

I was very impressed with the officer knowing that the cow on the road was a heifer .

Acting quickly, I dialled the number. I have to admit that I did feel a little awkward when the pleasant lady at the other end of the phone asked if there was a reference number. "Cow," I said.

Luckily, she found it rather amusing and, as she took my details, she suddenly blurted out: "Farmer Bryan! I've just been reading about you in the newspaper. I really hope the farm can survive these dreadful times."

I completed the call and agreed to go and meet the police out in the road. By the time I reached them, the team of officers had managed to get her back into the forest where she had come from. Luckily, on this occasion, it wasn't one of ours.

"It's taken over six weeks but I'm pleased to confirm that the bank have agreed to provide a loan through the Business Interruption Plan." Stuart had seen this all through and, without Tim and his tireless efforts, we would never have managed to obtain the help.

"My head is spinning, Stuart," I replied. "Could you please explain what this involves as it's all above my head at the moment?"

"Of course. It's all quite simple, really. The Government guarantees that you will receive a loan at a very low interest rate, possibly 2%, and it can be paid over a period of up to seven years. You'll never get a better offer than this," Stuart reassuringly informed me.

"Trouble is, that means we'll be paying off this debt for seven years. And how much will we receive? And what happens if we can't afford the payments?" I was creeping into negative thinking again.

"You and Dawn are the only ones who can make that decision. All I can say is that you'll never get a better offer," said Stuart bluntly. "If you wish to continue running the farm, I strongly recommend that you take it. Obviously, it's going to be tough. They won't confirm the amount that they will offer you until all the paperwork has been completed. Hopefully, you should be looking in excess of £100,000 and I'm trying to move this to enable you to reopen once the lockdown restrictions are lifted. As for guaranteeing the payments, they won't be taking any personal securities from you or Dawn, as you are a limited company. Oh, and just one other positive note: the bank has agreed to increase your overdraft to enable you to pay off some of the debts." Stuart finally concluded.

Quite clearly, this was a tremendous amount of information to take in. And I was going to need to relay all of it to Dawn.

"Bryan, I'll put that all in writing and call you once I get more news," Stuart promised. Full of thanks and praise, I said my goodbyes and went to find Dawn.

"That's an awful lot of money! How will we ever pay it back?" Dawn asked me as I gave her the good news.

"Well, it's either that or we simply retire and give it all up," I sharply responded. It would seem I'd made up my mind.

"That calf has become a real nuisance. He's going to have to go unless you can keep him in," I shouted as Renyard was chased around the yard with Charley and Hollie in pursuit.

"He's only playing!" said Hollie, trying to defend him.

"You're mean, Granddad. You can't sell him; he's part of the family," Charley added in support. "Can't we put him with the pygmy goats and see if he stays in there?"

I was becoming irritated and exhausted as I guided him into the paddock. "This calf has become well and truly spoilt by a certain member of our team. Look at him chasing the goats; he's become a liability." But my comments were being ignored. Things were looking a little brighter around the farm and Charley and Hollie weren't about to let me bring the mood down.

•

The upwards trajectory didn't stop there as we were soon in receipt of more good news. I'd had a phone call with Nicola at the Environmental Health department of New Forest District Council and I was extremely surprised about a sudden change of heart.

"Well, that was quick," I said to Dawn, my face beaming. "The Environmental Health has confirmed that we'll be able to reopen the Farm Shop during the next few weeks, as long as we submit a safety plan ensuring that the staff and customers will not be put at risk." Clearly there would be issues, but the thought of getting back to some form of normality was a great boost. "I'll contact Stewart at Splash Display to see if he can fix up a screen," I said, then paused. "Assuming that he's still able to work."

"Will Wayne and Rich want to come back that soon?" Dawn asked a little hesitantly.

"We can only ask them," I said with a shrug. "But they have been off for more than six weeks so hopefully they'll agree to. We really do need to get some income in, and it'll be helpful for the locals, too. Like Mrs Peracy said the other day, she can't wait to get back to some form of normality and be able to come and collect her milk and butter." My thoughts were getting back to normal – whatever that is.

Stewart sounded elated as he answered his mobile. "Well, that's great news," he said, the tone of his voice proving that he was ready to start work again. Like so many business owners, he had not worked for at least two months. The news of the relaxation of the lockdown regulations was truly welcomed. "I'll be there with my tape-measure in an hour," he confirmed.

Wayne, however, sounded less optimistic when we spoke to him. "Don't you think it's too soon?" he questioned.

"Well, not really. We do need to get started again. I know it may be a bit risky initially. We need to remain cautious about the health risks, and then there's the gamble of taking you off furlough and then not getting enough customers in to cover the wages. But that's a chance that we're prepared to take, if you are. After all, it may take weeks before we're able to actually open the doors, so we do have time to consider it."

I was trying to justify our decision to open up the Farm Shop to keep the business afloat. In doing so, I was hammering poor Wayne with a barrage of questions to see that it happened.

"Do you think the producers and wholesalers will be able to supply the stock? I already have assurance that Mole Valley will keep the poultry feed coming in. Can you ask the question as I need to let our customers know what's happening." I could feel desperation in the tone of my voice now, although I sensed that Wayne didn't share my enthusiasm just yet. But we had time to adjust and plan.

Opening the farm to the visitors was completely another matter. The complexity of the regulations and requirements in order to open the farm was daunting, to say the least. No matter what the media were saying, there was so much against us opening, it was soul-destroying. Certainly enough to dampen my new-found enthusiasm.

The appeal had now reached a staggering £42,000, but we were already eating into it and my concerns were mounting once again. Every day the farm gates remained closed meant another day's worth of costs in animal feed, bedding and utilities. Despite the generosity we'd seen, and the help we'd been able to secure, that was a finite resource. Would we ever get through this?

The whole country was desperate to get out and about, and being able to visit farms and parks would be hugely welcomed. However, the governing bodies, quite rightly, remained worried in case this dreaded virus flared up again. The number of daily cases seemed to be spiralling in certain parts of the country.

"So, Dad, when will you be opening the gates to the farm itself?" Aaron asked as we were drinking a beer on our front lawn. "Surely, that's possible now that we're able to meet in open spaces?" In theory, this was true. As long as the visitors kept their distances and stayed in their social groups then the growing perception was that we should be able to open the farm.

"Wish it was that simple," I started to explain. "Before we open, we have to ensure that the Environmental Health and insurance company are fully satisfied that we have put everything in place to make sure that all the visitors and staff are fully protected. In reality, that means that all buildings will have to be closed, therefore all activities will need to be outside. Social distancing will have to be enforced; hand gels throughout the farm; more screens, like we've put into the Farm Shop, will need to be installed. It's just a minefield. It's impossible as it stands at the moment."

Aaron shook his head at the enormity of the task ahead. "You know what, Dad, you're going to need another Speckled Hen."

Perks, our large saddleback sow, appeared to be getting bored in her pen. "Let's put Perks outside into the paddock. She can eat the weeds and we can throw over the veggies that have been dropped off," I suggested to Hollie.

So, with bucket in hand, Hollie encouraged the large sow to follow her to the paddock. Once there, Perks cleared the contents of the bucket with a single flick of her snout, destroyed the railed fence around the paddock and trotted her 220kg of weight back into the pen where she'd come from.

"There's no pleasing these animals," I said to Hollie as we watched in amazement.

It seemed strange, as I opened the car park gates in anticipation that there would be customers coming to walk into the farm shop once again.

Wayne helped Kerry and Dawn to set up an area at the side of the shop to enable them to continue their 'click and collect' service that they had become fond of. Wayne then positioned himself behind the perspex screen designed to protect him from anyone who may be carrying the virus. We were trying a number of ways to ensure that he and Richard were safe, including large stick-on footprints placed two metres apart on the floor to ensure that social distancing was maintained.

As Anita, our first customer, walked up the ramp, we all wanted to give her a hug – but, obviously, that was forbidden! My face lit up as I heard the first transaction being placed through the till which had been redundant for so long. We had considered only allowing card payments but decided that we should give the customers the opportunity to get rid of the cash they hadn't been able to use for so long.

The farm may not have been open yet, but this integral part of it was. And it felt good to see it.

13.

"Farm parks will be able to open on the 11th of June as long as there is no contact with animals and social distancing is maintained. There must not be access to any indoor play, all outdoor play equipment must be fogged at least twice a day, gift shops must remain closed, any food served on the premises must be served outside, and any toilets must be sterilised after each single use," explained Tom, the chairman of NFAN, as he gave us the information on a Zoom call.

My heart sank as I listened. I had been prompted to join the call to obtain more information after the local Southern Daily Echo reporter had told me the news that all farm parks would be able to open soon. The truth of it, though, was that opening would come with some heavy caveats.

The rules were there to protect visitors and staff alike, but the practical implementation of them was something else. They would all come at a greater cost, through additional staff and extra resources. Could it ever be economically viable?

I wasn't the only one to be disappointed as the Chairman resumed: "NFAN will do its utmost to persuade the government officials to reduce the stringent rules imposed on us. After all, we all know that the safest place to be in situations like this is in the open air."

Up to this point, Dawn and I had been paying the staff wages from our personal account and drawn the maximum from as many credit cards that we could use.

But there is a second Dawn in my life, although this one is in charge of our accounts. And she was calling with some good news. "Bryan, your first payment for the furloughed staff will be paid into your account during the next few days. This will be about £20,000. That will certainly help you. And, now it's set up, they'll be paying you on a monthly basis."

"That's taken about seven weeks for us to get this," I retorted bitterly. Often good news is delivered with some bad, as I was about to find out.

"The bad news, Bryan, is that you will now need to pay the National Insurance on the wages that have been paid," she continued.

"And I guess the VAT will still need to be paid," I sarcastically responded.

"Well, at the least you're not incurring any more VAT liabilities whilst there is very little income coming in," Dawn replied, looking for the silver lining. "The 5% threshold will help enormously once you're able to reopen again."

Dawn had been a tremendous support to us as we tried to juggle the expenditure and wages throughout this pandemic. With her calm yet sometimes bossy approach, she would research every new incentive that the Government had been throwing out at an alarming rate. I often wondered how the average business managed to absorb all the information landing on their computer screens.

The hot weather had made it extremely uncomfortable for most of the animals, especially the alpacas, as they were carrying about 4kg of fibre on their backs. This is the equivalent of us wearing a heavy winter coat during the summer months! This needed addressing.

The alpacas ran to the fence as Lara and Paige arrived with their equipment to shear them. Lara managed to catch Blossom first and pin her against the wall. It always amazes me how quickly these girls can turn the large creatures over and lie them on the floor, securing them in readiness of removing the entire fleece. Blossom was swearing loudly at them during the entire process. Whilst Lara sheared, Paige clipped the hooves and trimmed their teeth and, as they released each alpaca, a dose of wormer was administered into their mouths.

"Job done. They were well behaved today," Lara said with sweat pouring from her forehead as the last alpaca struggled to her feet. Glancing backwards, the alpaca gave the girls a disapproving glare as it headed out to the paddock to show off its new hairstyle to the other animals who had been watching over the fence.

Conscious of my own thick head of hair, I was tempted to ask them to give me a trim before they left.

"Bryan, is that another empty bottle of whiskey in the bin?" Dawn asked me cautiously.

"Yes, I filled the decanter up again this morning," I admitted.

"You drank that last one quickly. Surely it was only the other day that you topped the decanter up," she continued, watching for my reactions.

"Yes, I must admit, I did think that myself," I confessed. My normal nightly nightcap had become several glasses of the best Single Malt, which I prefer to drink without diluting with water. Worse, my normal one finger rule had recently become half a glass full. "I'd better reduce the amount I drink or else I'll be running out," I added. I thought I ought to admit to it being a problem before being told. "Mind you, it might be why I haven't gone down with Covid yet."

Did I sound convincing?

Planning for re-opening was taking up a lot of my time, not least with phone calls. Nicola, our local Environmental Health Officer, was one of many.

"Bryan, you know that I would really like to give you the go-ahead to open but DEFRA are waiting for the Minister of Culture to provide the guidance. Until this happens, we can't give you the go-ahead," Nicola explained.

"How long are we going to have to wait? It's been weeks since the other parks and open spaces were allowed to open." I could feel myself becoming agitated with the frustration of it all. "It seems that the government bodies are not working together like they should be," I continued.

"There are grants provided by New Forest District Council to help you cover some of your losses," Nicola said, cleverly changing the subject. "I'll send you a link to the website. Bryan, you really have to accept that this could go on much longer than we expected. This financial support is designed to help get you through. I'll keep in touch and you'll be the first one I call once we get any further information."

The gazebo in our garden had become our office and meeting room now that we were permitted to meet four other people from different bubbles – as long as we were outside.

"I'm becoming accustomed to this," I said as I poured a glass of beer out for Simon, our graphic designer, and Stewart, who makes our signs. Liza and Dawn sat in the sun, sipping on a gin and tonic. "I take it that you've all tested for Covid? Good, let's get to work. We need to work out a plan for what is required ready for opening," I said, starting the discussion. "The most important thing is that we must keep our staff and visitors safe. This will involve social distancing, so Simon and Stewart will need to come up with some signs to guide people around the farm, as well as markers to remind them to keep their distance. There will need to be lots of hand gel units around the farm as the soap and water is not adequate, according to the medical advisors."

"Surely that's nonsense," Liza butted in.

"I know but don't get me started on that. Apparently, soap and water is good enough for E. coli and cryptosporidium but not Covid. But never mind that. Let's take a walk around the farm and work out a plan." I was feeling enthusiastic and I wanted to share this with our team.

The car park was our first port of call. "We'll need signs to keep all visitors' cars two metres apart," I explained. This was in case two families were at adjacent cars at the same time.

"What size do they need to be?" Simon asked.

"As large as possible, with tough material, so people can't miss them. And that applies to every sign we install," I continued.

"Not wishing to be pessimistic, but this will increase the cost drastically. Have you considered using a cheaper material and smaller signs? It'll be a fraction of the cost," suggested Stewart, as Simon nodded his head in agreement.

"No, let's do this properly. We don't know how many months or even years we'll need them for. We don't wish to go through all this again." Dawn and Liza were in favour of this.

As we crossed the road, Liza asked, "Will you be operating an online booking system or taking payment at the entrance? Obviously, you'll need to restrict visitor numbers."

"Yes, that's a job on your list. That's a condition that DEFRA have insisted should be in place, so it'll be online booking and, depending on what system we settle for, people will have to show pre-paid tickets. Definitely no cash payments at all. Could you please liaise with Alex to see if it's possible? " I was happy to delegate this job. Alex builds and maintains our website and I presumed we were setting him quite a challenge with that one.

"This is where it's going to be difficult," Dawn commented as we reached the farm entrance. "We won't be able to deal with all the visitors through this window. We're going to need another place to receive them, too. How on earth will we be able to fit another counter here."

Stewart was quick to answer: "Why not just put a table out here? If you're going to be scanning pre-paid tickets then we'll just need to ensure that there's wi-fi coverage out here."

So far, so good. I felt we were making progress, and it all felt achievable – as long as the technology was going to work as we pictured it.

"Now, at this point, we require some very large signs stating all the rules that people will need to follow while on the farm." I looked at Simon. "This is where we need to make things bright, colourful and fun." Simon likes a challenge and has never let us down. "No problem," he said with a very big smile. "You can leave that with me. I'm going to enjoy this one." He was clearly looking forward to tackling it. The guidance we would have to follow was lengthy, and it was one thing getting the staff to keep to it, but quite another to encourage the visitors. People would need constant reminders to keep a safe distance from other families, and for that we decided a regular footprint graphic needed to be painted on the ground.

"But that's a lot of footprints," I said. "We'll probably need in excess of 200. That's a huge job for somebody to cope with."

Before I had finished my sentence, Simon said, "I have two strong lads at home who are doing nothing at the moment. Between Stewart and me, we'll sort out some templates and Adam and Luke can get cracking," he volunteered.

Next I needed to address the biggest challenge. "The toilets are going to be the real problem," I stated. "There is absolutely no guidance at the moment on how often they should be cleaned or how many visitors can enter them at any one time so I really don't know what signs to put here," I said as we stood next to the toilet block.

"Well, considering it's a family attraction and children will require supervision in the toilets, why don't we just have a 'one family group only' sign? That way we've covered ourselves. If they require cleaning after each family then that's what will have to be done." Liza's idea seemed like an excellent solution.

"I can do cartoons of family groups of animals for those signs," Simon suggested with a smile.

"What are the rules about the outdoor play equipment?" Stewart asked.

"Ah," I replied. "That's a minefield of its own." We headed down to the silent and still play area to get a look. "The requirement is that all the equipment will have to be disinfected between each use. Then, I believe, it will require fogging at least twice a day. As for the trampolines, they can only be used by one family at a time." I was sounding pretty depressing now. Hardly the definition of care-free outdoor fun. "But that's not going to stop us opening. We'll find a way to do it, I'm sure," I added, trying to sound a little more upbeat.

As we walked back through the farm, though, I was pleased with how it was all coming together. "We've had a very constructive meeting and it looks as though we have a plan. Are you all ready to make this work?" I asked with grin.

"Quotes will be out tomorrow," Stewart answered.

"And I'll put together some roughs so you can see what I'm suggesting," added Simon.

"I'll be in touch with Alex and proofread all the material once it's completed. And I'll get a press release into draft form," Liza confirmed.

"I dread to think how much all this will cost," Dawn said, speaking the words we were all thinking.

"Well, it has to be done," I stated plainly. "We'll just have to look at how it will be funded later." I was putting a brave face on it, because, one way or another, I was determined to get the farm open once more.

Mabel, the small Kunekune pig, had given birth to four very small piglets that morning. "I guess she decided that, as there are no visitors, she would have a smaller litter," I joked.

The piglets needed to be injected with an iron supplement and checked they didn't have any hernias, so Hollie assisted me. "This is good timing as I've just sold two from the last litter as pets to a family in Surrey," I said. No matter how many times I see a litter of piglets born, it always amazes me how quickly they grow.

The cycle of births and deaths is familiar to all farmers. As wonderful as it was to welcome the piglets, it was then soul-destroying to find Frankie, the mallard drake, curled up in the corner of the duck house.

He'd died during the night in his sleep. Frankie had been brought to the farm twelve years earlier as an orphan. When he was young, he would fly around the farm showing off to all the other ducks. We never clipped his wings so he could fly away and join other ducks if he wished, but he seemed quite content to stay at Longdown with his 150 Khaki Campbells and Cherry Valley wives. RIP Frankie.

"Ian has called and asked if he can come and have a chat," Dawn told me as I fed the ducks.

"Did he say what he wanted to talk about?" I asked.

"No, but he said he would like a chat today so I suggested coming out at lunchtime. We can have a sandwich out in the gazebo," Dawn responded.

"What will happen to the Mobile Farm?" Dawn asked, referring to the collection of animals Ian took out to schools, shows and events.

"I have no idea. It's going to be very a very long time before we'll be able to go to a school or village fete again. It may well be the end of it. That's probably what Ian wants to chat about," I said as I closed the duck pen door.

I could tell by the body language that it was not good news as Ian walked across the lawn.

"A pint?" I asked.

"Yes, please," was the expected answer.

Dawn went to hug Ian like she would normally do but stopped herself just in time. "This is all strange," she said. "I just can't get used to it. How is Peta?" she enquired.

"She's coping very well, thanks," Ian replied. "The reason I wanted to see you is that we've decided to move to St Ives to spend more time with the family. We'll need to wrap up the Mobile Farm." I could tell that this was difficult for Ian to tell us.

"We fully understand. It must have been a difficult decision. But your family must come first, always. Thank you for letting us know so soon."

Ian had been a major part of Longdown. His organisational skills were second to none and he had a wonderful way with people, coupled with his wicked sense of humour. We knew that all the staff would miss him. His wife, Peta, and little Quinn had become very close friends to us. We would miss him dreadfully.

As he finished his can of Speckled Hen, we broke all the rules by shaking hands and he gave Dawn a big hug.

It was easy to think that we were working towards things being back to exactly what they were pre-lockdown, but many changes, such as Ian going, meant things promised to be very different. Losing Ian was a blow, and it wasn't to be the only one

Not long after, as Jess and I stepped onto the farm for the first time that day, she raced to the main gates, barking and growling, the hair on the back of her neck standing up on end. This was uncharacteristic for her. She stood at the gate, refusing to move.

I assumed that she had seen a fox or something and didn't take much notice. I didn't want her crossing the road to where our car park stands so I slid through the side gate and headed across. But, as I reached the car park's large metal gates, I was horrified to see debris strewn all over the ground.

My first thought was that someone had fly-tipped a large amount of rubbish, so, crossly, I went to pick it up and put it into a pile. But, gazing to my right revealed the true nature of what had happened here. The kennels had been stolen.

As you would expect, as a working farm where you come to meet and feed the animals, we can't allow dogs to enter. Nor can we expect people to leave them in their cars. The solution is a block of kennels, in the shade, that visitors can return to throughout the day. At least, that's what we had until last night.

I phoned 111 to report it to the police, only to encounter a long five-minute message of what to do if you were reporting a case of breaching Covid rules. I soon discovered that the thieves had forced one of the gates at the bottom of the car park to gain entry and managed to dismantle and remove the entire block of kennels.

When I told Liza a short time later, she suggested finding a photo of the kennels and taking another of the mess they left behind. "I'll post it on social media," she suggested, in the hope it would help us track it down.

Now, I'm not a fan of social media, but the appeal had been boosted by it and I couldn't deny its power. Once again it proved it had some advantages over the old-fashioned newspapers as the response we had was simply outstanding.

Unfortunately, though, the kennels were never found.

"At last, we'll be able to open our gates later in July," I declared to Hollie and Charis. "It's subject to stringent codes of practice being adhered to, but the

Culture Secretary has given the nod for open farms to resume operating. We're a step closer to opening again." I had just received the news from NFAN, but Hollie and Charis were looking at me dubiously. Perhaps they didn't want to get their hopes up.

But I was buoyant. "Steve and Terry will finish rolling the chalk in the calf pen. And Dawn has organised some help to finish off the painting around the farm."

"I daren't stay still for too long at the moment for fear of being given a fresh coat," Kerry jokingly butted in.

Although we had been granted the opportunity to get things tidy and refreshed, it wasn't quite as straightforward as opening the gates when we were ready. "I'll phone the Environmental Health and see if we can have a site visit," I explained. "Then we'll need to undertake a risk assessment for the insurers to approve. There's so much to get sorted in such a short space of time." I guess Kerry could hear the excitement in my voice.

"Dad, don't get too carried away. They could change their minds. They've done it before," she cautioned.

"Thanks for the reminder but let's think positively," I responded. But I knew only too well that anything could happen between now and then.

THE LONGDOWN LOCKDOWN

14.

"Could you please keep an eye on Maisie?" I asked Charley. "I'm on a very important Zoom call. We're discussing how we can open the farm again. I really don't want to miss it." Charley was looking delighted to be given this important task. "All you need to do is keep looking over the fence to see if the kid's feet are showing from her back end. She's a strong goat so I'm sure that she'll manage to push this one out herself but you just need to keep an eye on her."

Charley didn't need asking twice and dashed off to the pygmy goat paddock, leaving me to close the door behind her. She had never been given so much responsibility before.

This left me to concentrate on what mattered. As I was discussing what procedures we had put into place with the other delegates, the office door flew open. "Come on, Granddad, you have to come outside," Charley was screaming frantically. "The baby's stuck. You have to come out now."

There were 65 people witnessing this. "It's pointless trying to reason with Charley," I explained to everyone watching. "I need to sort this out," and so I made my excuses and left.

"Well done, Charley. You were right," I said once I was able to take stock of the situation. "The kid's nose is blue. If we don't get it out soon, it'll die. This leg has to go back inside to enable us to bring the other leg in line with it, then hopefully we can pull the poor little thing out."

Charley's face was now looking desperate as I tried to manoeuvre the legs.

"My hand is too big to get in between so you'll have to put your hand in and try to shift the other leg," I said. But before I had finished explaining what to do, Charley had nudged me aside and was managing to squeeze her hand through the narrow gap. There was determination on her face as she wriggled her fingers around the spindly legs of the tiny kid. "Granddad, I can feel the other leg. What shall I do now?" she shouted at the top of her voice, even though I was standing alongside her.

"Firstly, calm down," I advised. "Then, gently push the leg back inside."

"But we have to get the poor thing out. I'm not pushing it back in." She was becoming hysterical because of the enormity of the situation – aware that a life was quite literally in her hands.

"You won't be able to pull it out until both legs are together inside her. Now, please do as you're told." I forced my voice to remain calm and measured.

"I have both legs now, shall I pull?" Her excitement was becoming overwhelming, as the tiny kid dropped onto the grass.

"Clear the mucus from the nostrils!" It was me who was shouting now as there was no sign of life in the little body. I held the kid upside down as Charley desperately rubbed its rib cage to remove any liquid from the lungs. Then I swung the newborn around in the air.

"Don't hurt it, Granddad. You're being cruel," Charley shouted.

I didn't respond, just found a short piece of straw and gave it to Charley to push up the kid's nostril to make it sneeze. The look on this teenager's face when the kid coughed and opened its eyes was priceless.

"I'm sorry that I had to rush off. I had a birth to attend to," I quietly said as I resumed the Zoom call a short time later.

"More importantly, what did she have?" Sally, one of the NFAN members, enquired.

"A little boy." I was pleased to inform them that he was fit and well.

Getting through to anyone on an automated phone system at New Forest District Council offices is an art in itself.

"Say the name of the person required," the automated attendant demanded. Even though I spoke slowly, the attendant responded, "Name not recognised, please try again."

Now, I know I have a slight lisp but surely it should understand me. This was not going very well but what I didn't know was, once I did get through, things were going to get worse. I rate Nicola very highly as a down-to-earth and practical Environmental Health Officer and thought that this phone call would be just routine. I figured that once I told her what we would be doing to reopen the farm, she would simply sign it off.

This was not to be the case.

"When will you be able to come and do a site visit?" was my leading question.

"Unfortunately, we're all working from home and will not be able to undertake any site visits until at least September," she cautiously replied.

"But it tells me in the guidance information sheet that an inspection by a local EHO is required before any establishment can open their gates. Are you telling me that we cannot open until you are allowed to resume site visits?" My voice was now becoming uncharacteristically aggressive. Why was everything two steps forward, one step back?

"Bryan, you know darn well that I'll do my best to help you. However, it seems that you have access to more information than we've received. Please forward all the details that you have and we'll try to work out a solution." Nicola was using her natural charm and well-rehearsed customer care training to calm the situation down.

I took a deep breath and explained all of the work that we had undertaken before asking her advice on the best types of hand gel to use and how we could fog the play equipment. She listened intently throughout. Then, without any warning, she dropped a bombshell.

"You do know, Bryan, that it's unlikely that you'll be able to operate any animal activities at all because of the risk to your visitors," she said firmly.

I felt like I'd had a knife in my heart. For our farm, that would be disastrous.

"That's ridiculous. It won't be worth opening the farm if we don't have animals available to feed. What's the point of going to a farm to just look at the animals. That's not what we're about." Once again my voice was becoming louder.

"Well, let's wait until the next set of guidance is issued," she suggested. "But, until then, please don't attempt to open, otherwise you'll almost certainly be prosecuted. We'll be in touch."

And that was that.

•

I had been communicating with Ed from the New Forest Wildlife Park, the visitor attraction next door, throughout this pandemic. It was beneficial to both of us to share experiences and ideas. He had obviously had dealings with the EHO as well as they also covered his Health & Safety.

"Ed, I see that you intend to open next week. How on earth have you managed to obtain permission?" I asked.

"We're classified as a zoo as we have a zoo licence and, because our visitors don't have contact with the animals, we've been granted permission to open," he said with some sympathy. He knew only too well how desperate we were to open.

"But what about the EHO inspection? How have you got around that?" I enquired. "I was told they couldn't come out until at least September!"

"That wasn't even mentioned in the guidance that we were issued," he replied.

"This is so annoying," I said through gritted teeth. But I couldn't deny him his good fortune in being able to open. I wished him good luck with it all.

Richard, a Dorset goat farmer, called to see if we were ready to take on the goat kids yet. "Could you hold on to them for a week or so? By then, we should have confirmation on what day we'll be able to open," I asked, knowing that he had already kept these kids back a long time for us.

"Sorry, Bryan, but I'm desperate for space as there's another batch due to kid down next week. I'll need to move some out before the weekend. If not, they'll have to be put down as no one else wants them now." The sincerity in his voice made me aware that he wasn't bluffing; he meant it.

"Are you able to deliver some or should I arrange transport?" I asked.

"I'm delivering milk to Wellow later tonight. I can put some in the back of the truck, if you want." His tone had changed immensely. No farmer enjoys putting animals down, especially when they're so small.

"I'll break the news to Hollie. She may have forgotten how to feed them," I joked.

I went to find her to give her the news. "Hollie, we have twenty goat kids arriving tonight. Could we have a pen ready before you go home and I'll feed them when they arrive," I said, trying not to make too big a deal of the subject.

"That's fantastic news! I can't wait to have goats back in the barn!" she said with glee. "It's seemed so strange without them. Let me know when they come in and Charis and I will come back to feed them." This wasn't the response I was expecting. "Does this mean that we'll definitely be opening soon?" she asked.

"Wish I had an answer to that question," I replied. "Oh, by the way, there will be another batch of fifty goats arriving next week. If I hadn't agreed to take them, then they would have been put down." I knew that this would tug Hollie's heart strings.

So it looked like we were going to have goats, but no visitors. And even if we got visitors, they weren't going to be allowed to feed the goats. It was all feeling as if getting to where I wanted to be would forever be out of my grasp.

Regardless, I ploughed on.

I called Shaun, our risk assessor. "It's good to hear from you," he said happily. "Hopefully, you're calling to arrange a visit?"

"Yes, but not sure when we'll be able to open," I grumbled. It was hard to hide my disappointment.

"I know you must be tearing your hair out," sympathised Shaun. I wish one department would listen to the other, then maybe we could all be in a better position. If it's any help to you, I've been told by a very reliable source that open farms will be able to reopen on the 26th of July, subject to a national reduction in Covid cases. So, let's all aim for that date."

This was promising.

"The bad news is, we're not allowed site visits until the beginning of August, so let me pencil in a visit then. As long as you keep me in touch with what arrangements you've made and work closely with the EHO, then all will be good," Shaun explained. "Just one word of warning, Bryan: don't fall out with the Environmental Health Officer. They could close you down just as quickly as you open those gates. Be warned." Obviously, Shaun had heard about my frustrations.

The smile on Julie's face said it all as we worked out ways that we could open the Tea Room and Kiosk in just a few weeks' time. Julie was the Tea Room manager and the Tea Room was her domain – and she'd missed it. It was currently looking better than ever, but it wouldn't be reopening in quite the manner of its former self.

"No one will be able to eat in here. This will have to be turned into a takeaway area," I explained as we studied the surroundings.

Dawn and Simon were sliding tables across the floor, making an incredible amount of noise as they planned how to create a pathway through to the counter.

"You'll have a screen in front of the till to prevent any germs being passed through to you; all payments will be by card, absolutely no cash," I continued.

Simon and Dawn had moved on to the chairs. As the Tea Room was reshuffled, ideas and suggestions were being made and discarded in an effort to work out the best way to manage the flow of people in and out.

"I guess I'm going to have let you decide this between yourselves," I said as I took a call from Jon at the cleaning company.

"It's great news to hear that you're hoping to open again soon, Bryan, and I'm pleased that you wish us to continue with the cleaning," said Jon.

"Are you able to supply someone to keep the toilets sterile, as well as the wash basins and picnic benches around the farm. It's going to be a relentless task," I said hopefully. This role would be key to us getting the farm back on its feet.

"Yes, that won't be a problem," he confidently confirmed. "We've just interviewed a great chap; his name is Craig. He'll take that on. If he comes in about seven in the morning and stays until lunchtime, would that suit you?" Jon asked.

This was music to my ears. "Perfect," I said.

"He'll be good with the visitors and keep the place safe," reassured Jon.

Step by step, we were getting there.

My 'to do list' was getting longer and longer and I was having great delight in crossing off tasks that I had completed or delegated. But it seemed the more I got done, the more was added to it.

One of the major hurdles had been the online booking system, essential for us to be able to not only operate without cash, but to manage exact numbers coming on to the farm.

Dawn and the front desk team were all ready to have a training session on how to use the new QR code scanners which Alex, our website designer, had helped organise.

"All I can say is good luck," I said to Alex, "because I know that they're going to give you a hard time."

"Not a problem, I like a challenge," he chuckled. Alex and Liza had been working tirelessly to create the booking system. We had tried another company previously but that had been a complete disaster, with the wrong equipment being supplied and very poor customer support. To say that that experience was stressful is an understatement. However, we'd now known Alex for a long time and he knew just what we required. His ability to explain the workings of modern technology to a group of dinosaurs had won us all over.

Luckily for us, when Alex had started to ask what wi-fi coverage we had at the farm, to ensure the scanners could be used effectively, we simply gave him Paul's number. He's a whiz-kid on all these types of things, and the pair of them could talk to each other in a language I could only hope to understand.

The training course, thankfully, went extremely well. Alex explained to Dawn, Wendy, Julie, Steph and Alice that there was very little difference in the process of scanning the entry vouchers than purchasing something online – something they had all become accustomed to during lockdown.

At long last, I felt that we were getting back to what we were good at.

The goat shed was now nearly full, and we had another batch of calves arriving that would keep Mike busy as he returned from being furloughed.

"I'm really glad to be back," he grinned. "But you'll need to be kind to me as I've put on a bit of weight and my muscles are basically seized up! Having all this time off hasn't helped at all," he admitted, struggling to lift a bag of milk powder over the hurdles.

James, who was one of our volunteers during lockdown, was happy to be back cleaning out all the chicken and duck pens although his smile did drop a little when I told him that there would be another fifty ducks arriving later that day.

Because of Charley's success in kidding the pygmy goat, we had promoted her to main pygmy goat stockperson. She was now in charge – obviously backed up by Hollie – of ensuring that the pregnant mums were well cared for. Although, I wasn't so sure if I agreed with her when she told me, "We're not allowed to sell any of the kids this year. I want to keep them all!"

THE LONGDOWN LOCKDOWN

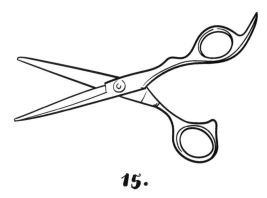

15.

"We have such an amazing group of friends," I said to Dawn as she was making rolls and cutting up cake for Steve, Bijan, Phil and Pete. We simply couldn't have got all this together without all their help and support.

"That's so true," Dawn agreed. "But how on earth can we repay them for all the hours that they've put in?"

They had installed the thirty-odd hand sanitisers and secured the vast number of necessary signs. The small signs on the picnic tables alone must have taken hours. And there was creating the safe place for eating in the marquee.

"Just having them here to chat to us has been so uplifting," she said.

"I think the best way to repay them is to get that food into their tummies," I said as I helped to carry out a tray. "Come on, gents, here's your wages."

The Chadwick family were also a tremendous support; no matter what job I asked them to do, they did it willingly and without any reimbursement. Luke and Adam had indeed painted the footprints around the farm and didn't even raise an eyebrow when I said – following Environmental Health suggestions – that there must now be a one-way system so all the directional signs that they had painted had to be changed!

Dawn seemed very excited when she shouted across the yard to me. "I've just heard that hairdressers are allowed to start again in two weeks' time. You need to get your haircut booked in quickly because they'll soon get booked up," she said with some urgency.

"Okay, I'll do it right away," I said, thinking that I would get brownie points for acting so quickly.

"Ray, I need to make an appointment." I was expecting to be told that the diary was full.

"No problem, Bryan. I've booked you in for the first day that we open. I saw a photo of you on Facebook the other day and thought to myself that's a bad advert for our business. So I've booked you in with Dan," he responded.

"Now, that's what I call excellent customer service," I said as I thanked him. "During the past twelve weeks I've had endless offers to shear, trim and cut my hair from all sorts of people. I've been called Worzel Gummidge, Brian May and even Shaggy Sheep Dog."

Mind you, I was grateful I still had hair to grow, especially at my age.

July the 4th was set for the big day, but before that it was time for another chat with Environmental Heath.

"Bryan, I know that you intend to open next Saturday and thank you for all the photos you have sent me showing what you have put in place. But there is an additional guidance paper that I have just received and it does indeed state that there must not be any animal contact at open farms and all indoor areas must remain closed. That doesn't include the Tea Room, as that is covered by another set of guidance and I know you've followed the procedure on that that we've agreed on."

Nicola was confirming my worst fears and I was starting to see red again.

"Now, the barn which houses the goats has Yorkshire boarding on two sides and an open front at the entrance. Surely that's not classed as an indoor area; there is more ventilation in there than most outdoor facilities. I think this is totally unfair!" I was trying to hold back the anger in my voice.

"Rules are rules and I'm only relaying what instructions I've been given," she replied abruptly, and she was absolutely right.

"Okay. What if I open the gates and allow the visitors to wander around the farm with all the animals double fenced, so they can't be touched? As long as all buildings are closed, will that be acceptable?" I was now trying to come up with an alternative.

"Yes, that will be fine, but please remember: no animal contact at all. If we have a report that you are allowing animal contact then we'll have no alternative but to close you down." Nicola's voice was now sounding official.

Irrespective of where the rule was coming from, I thought it was madness. I just couldn't see the logic in it, and I couldn't shake the thought that I should just carry on as normal. After all, the EHO were not allowed site visits for a while.

"Dad, you can't do that! If they've told you not to let visitors feed the goats, you mustn't let them. It will give you bad publicity," Kerry insisted. "Even if we have to wait a week or two before opening, surely it's safer that way." Kerry simply did not agree with my plan.

"You know what your father's like: he breaks all the rules or changes them to suit him," Dawn said, smiling knowingly at her.

I relayed the news to Liza. "That's ridiculous!" shouted Liza down the phone. "Why wasn't this made clear to you in the first place? Typical government officials. How can you open something like Longdown without the access to the animals? It's madness."

"Calm down, young lady. Sounds like you're more angry than me," I said, butting in. "I have a plan but I'm not telling anyone what it is yet or else you may try to talk me out of it."

"Don't do anything silly!" Liza warned me. "And where does that leave us with what I put out on social media tonight. You've only two days left before you open," I could tell that Liza had a hint of panic in her voice.

"Simply say that we will be opening, however there will be certain restrictions imposed on us by the Government. Assure all our visitors and staff that Longdown will be a very safe environment. Please don't mention animal feeding or chick handling at all," I said. "The good news is that we are able to open the outdoor play area as long as it's only used by family bubbles and that the equipment is cleaned on a hourly basis. And, guess what, we now have a decision on the toilets: cleaning every half an hour is adequate." I was feeling on a roll. "Let's get those gates open," I said.

"You're the boss," Liza said, warming to my enthusiasm.

Our friends Phil and Steve had been a great sounding board for me during those difficult weeks of lockdown so I asked them both in for a cup of coffee to discuss the Environmental Health's latest enforcements. I knew darn well that they would be disappointed to hear that, despite all their hard work, we would not be able to open fully.

"Maybe reduce your entry charge to compensate for the reduced activities," Phil suggested.

"But that's not fair on our season ticket holders," I quickly responded.

"You know my feelings on that!" barked Steve. "You haven't charged enough, all these years. You give excellent value for money and your visitors should expect to pay more." I knew Steve would take this stance.

I had a suggestion. "How about if we open and bring the chicks outside and the goats to the fence? We can then allow the visitors to feed them as they'll be outside."

"Have they told you that visitors are unable to touch the animals or that they cannot go into the sheds?" Phil enquired.

"You know what, I haven't seen any guidance on that matter and if I did I'm sure that it could be deleted from the computer," I said cheekily. "My discussion with Environmental Health wasn't recorded, so the answer to your question, I guess, is no!" I tried not to make any eye contact as I said this.

"Well, there you go, then," Phil chipped in, winking at Steve.

But being cavalier with the rules and guidance didn't go down so well with Kerry when I voiced my plan to her and Dawn.

"Don't expect me to visit you in jail when you get caught, Dad," was Kerry's response as I told her.

"Best keep this to ourselves or it may get back to the authorities," I said conspiratorially as I went to answer the phone in the office. My heart jumped when I heard who it was.

It was Nicola from Environmental Health. "Bryan, we've been discussing your situation in the office this morning and we've decided that you can allow your visitors to feed and touch the animals as long as they are outside. No one is to go inside the buildings. Is that clear?" Knowing that I would be pleased, she added, "Good luck."

Waves of relief washed over me. "I could kiss you, but better not. You know, because of Covid," I said, full of emotion.

"Wow, what a difference a phone call makes," Kerry said as she watched me punch my fist in the air.

16.

"There are over 300 people booked in today. I know it's not going to give us much income as it's mostly only season ticket holders but at least the gates will be open," I said to Dawn as we ate our breakfast.

"I'm just worried about how we're going to cope with the scanners. How will we be able to get the information we need to keep if they don't work?" Dawn was now sounding a little nervous, which was quite understandable. We were finally at the point we'd been working so hard towards, and there was so much riding on it.

"You'll be fine. You have Alice out there with you, and she's good with technology and great with people. She'll help you." I tried to sound reassuring but it wasn't working. There was just so much that could go awry.

"It's alright for you. You won't have to put up with the angry visitors if things go wrong," she said, heading towards the entrance.

I'd been waiting for this moment for 119 days, since the start of lockdown, and now that it had arrived I was full of a mixture of relief, anxiety and excitement, combined with the uncertainty of what was going to happen.

How did our staff feel? Were they worried? Did they feel safe?

Judging by the comments made at a recent team meeting, they all appeared to be behind us, but I couldn't help but be concerned.

As I walked around the farm, following the directional footprints, I could see the adults wearing face coverings and gelling their hands every few minutes, the children laughing and screaming with joy, and the orderly, safely distanced queuing to join in with the activities that Longdown is so well known for.

Even the animals seemed happier having the visitors return.

I knew that, without the support from the 1700 families, friends and businesses, and even complete strangers, that together raised £42,000 for our appeal, well, we wouldn't have been able to bridge the gap from then until now. That amazing £42,000, and the words of encouragement which kept us sane during those past 119 days, had kept Longdown going.

Seeing young Farmer Sam being pushed by his carers towards the goat shed made me realise just how many people benefit from being with the animals.

And there were Abbie and her growing calf, Renyard. Strange to think just how much we'd been through in that young animal's short life to date.

As I heard "Farmer Bryan" being shouted from the tractor ride that Lester was taking around the field, I felt a blossoming of pride at what Dawn and I had achieved with the help of so many people.

We are so truly grateful to each and every single one of them.

Afterword

Of course, that wasn't the last of it. There were two further lockdowns, used to help contain the spread of the virus, although these didn't have quite the same impact as the first. We were learning to deal with it by then.

Lou managed to enlighten a difficult year by providing us with our first grandson, Arthur, on the 19th November 2020.

This book is just meant to reflect our experiences at Longdown. The wider community – indeed, the wider world – felt its impact in so many different ways, with the aggravation, heartache and loss that it brought. But those are other people's stories, and this one was mine.

It's quite likely that I've got some of the time-line out of order. You'll have to forgive me. If you really must point out my errors then you'll find me more receptive to it over a pint of Speckled Hen.

I am quite sure that I've forgotten to acknowledge people that I really should have – there were so many of you that helped in countless ways with your own particular expertise, counsel, knowledge or friendship. If I have forgotten to mention you then please do accept my heartfelt apologies.

Thank You

Longdown Activity Farm is open and welcoming visitors today
as a direct result of the funds donated to our 'Help Feed The Animals' campaign
during the 2020 Covid-19 pandemic.

Our heartfelt and humble thanks are extended to the wonderful people listed
below, and also to a large number of donors who wish to remain anonymous.

Bryan, Dawn, Kerry and Charley Pass

Alya Abdar	Chris Ashley-Manns	Jane Barber	Colin Bath
Melanie Ackrill	Scott Ashmore	Nikki Barber	Ryan Bath
Lyndsey Adamek	Sarah Aspland	Helen Barker	Gill Bath-Hodgson
Danielle Adams	John Astbury	Michelle Barker	Peter Bayliss
Susan Adams	Nicky Atkins	Ann Barlow	Sarah Baylis
Sabina Aiuto	Charlotte Atkinson	Rob Barlow	Jo Beal
Beccy Alberry	Luke Atkinson	Crystal Barnard	Julie Beanland
Chloe Alexander	Kay Audoire	Lisa Barnard	Julie Beaumont
Guy Alexander	Julie Austin	Gill Barnes	Katy Beazley
Sharon Allcroft	Carla Avery	Katie Barnes	Claire Beckett
Meryl Allderidge	Pauline Avery	Heather Barnett	Rachel Beckingham
Peter Allen	The Azors	Helen Barrett	James Beer
Sarah Allfree	Lauren Babbidge	Anabela Barrie	Margaret Belcher
Christine Ames	Fiona Bach Roberts	Dawn Barron	Zoe Bellows
Richard Anderson	Christine Backshell	Lisa Barrow	Dale Benfield
Steve Anderson	Karen Bacon	Marie Barrow	Debra Bennett
Linda Angel	Emma Bailey	Elizabeth Barry	Emma Bennett
Amanda Ansell	Linda Bailey	Nicole Barry	Emma Bennett
Jack Ansell	Liz Bailey	Mike Bartlett	Jeremy Bennett
Michelle Appleby	Jessica & Elliot Baker	Peter Bartlett	Lorraine & Roly
Judith Archbold	Matt Baker	Rachel Bartlett	Bennett
Jade-Marie Archer	Melanie Baker	Andy & Diane	Wendy Bennett
Laura Archer	Mike Baker	Bartram	Kirsten Bermingham
Millie Arfman	Kirsty Balicao	Nina Basset	Lisa Berryman-
Rosie Arkell	David Ball	Carly Batchelor	Spender
Julieanne Arnold	Helen Barber	Julie Batchelor	Graham Bethel

David Betteridge
Alexander & Ann
Bezance
Keith Biddiscombe
Hilary Billinge
Paul Biddle
Karen Bidwell
Kelly Biles
Elaine Bird
Paul Bird
Rosie Bishop
Kate Bjedov
Loz Blackburn
Vanessa & Paul
Blacker
Kayleigh Blackford
H Blair
India Blake
Alice Blake-Hausen
Val & Ian Bland
Donna Blandford
Steve Blandford
Susan Blandford
Suzanne Bloomfield
Carrie Blythe
Rowena Bocock
Darren Boden
Sarah Bomd
Rachel Bonathan
Carole Bond
Mary Bond
Karen Boog
Andy Boorman
Elliot Bourne
Amanda Bowen
Lisa Bowen
Nickie Bowen
Diane Bower
Anna Bowers
Andrew Bown
Amber & Dan Box
Marjorie Boyle
Dave & Rose Brading
Christine Bradley
Samantha Bradley

Sabine Braines
Caroline Bray
Val Bray
Dawn Brechin
Connor Breen
Denise Breen
Sarah Brennan
Nikki Brigg
Anthony Brisdion
Sarah Brisdion
Lucy Broadbridge
Diane Bromley
Jason Brombley
Sharon Brombley
Ju Broom
Julianne Broom
Kristina Broomfield
Gemma Broster
Jane Brown
Lizzie Brown
Mary Brown
Rebecca Brown
Rosalind & David
Brown
Stu & Claire Brown
Sue Brown
Suzanne Brown
Carl Browning
Emma Browning
Rebecca Browning
Sara & Mike
Browning
Cath Bryant
Joelle Buck
Diana Buckell
Lee-Anne Budd
Jo Bull
Charlotte Bullen
Joe Bullock
Annemarie Bundy
Clare Burch
Louisa Burch
Brad Burgess
Dan Burgess
Tracy Burden

Jenny Burnage
Will Burns
Liza Burrows
Maria Burrows
Lauren Burton
Anna Butler
Caroline Butler
Lisa Butler
Michelle Butler
Marina Butlin
Helen Butt
Jade Buwembo
Pearl Byrne
Abigail Cacia
Jayne Calvert
Emma Cameron
Rachael Campbell
Cherith Campbell-
Bell
Julie Capponi
Mathew Card
Samantha Card
Gillian Carpenter
Gary, Julie & Rachel
Carr
Laura Carr
Hazel Carter
Joanne Carter
Katie Carter
Rebecca Carter
Melissa Catten
Sharon Catton
Nicola & Jessica
Cavanagh
The Chadwick Family
Anne Chalk
Hannah Chalk
James Chalk
Wendy Challice
Vicki Chamberlain
Jo Chant
Martin Charles
Helen Charge
Amy Chase
Mrs Chase

Gemma Cheeseman
Susan Cheffings
Ann & Steve Chester
Ross Chester
Liz Chick
Sarah Chipperfield
Anna Christelis
Daphne Christelis
Helen Chrzanowski
Valerie Clack
Maureen Claridge
Amy Clark
Hannah Clark
Jodie Clark
Jody Clark
Karen Clark
Thomas Clark
Tracy Clark
Alison Clarke
Lindsay Clarke
Ray Clarke
Sam Clarke
Tracy Clasper
Cheryl Clease
Chris Clemson
Alison Clifford
Tom Clifford
Janine Close
Tony Close
Greg Coak
Tristan Coaker
Laura Coakley
Sharon Coakley
Gilly Cobbin
Elisha Cochrane
Jennifer Coggle
Jack Cole
Megan Cole
Rob Cole
Steve Cole
Anna Coles
The Coles
Frankie Colling
Ben Collins
Elissa Collins

Kerry Collins	Daniel Cunnington	Vicky Dixon	Tabitha English
Iain & Kelly Collins	Michelle Curtis	Julie Dobbing	Charlotte Eustace
Michelle Collins	Scott Curtis	Sandie Dodds	Ali Evans
Paul Collins	Sue Curtis	Hayley Dodman	Deborah Evans
Alison Collinson	Trudy Curtis	Marie Donnachie	Emma Evans
Judith Collis	Danielle Czauderna	Anne Donnan	Sarah Evans
Steven Comer	Melanie Dando	Kelly-Anne Donnelly	Amanda Everett
Susan Compton	Amanda Daniel	Claire Dossett	Katie Everett
Catherine Connett	Anne Marie & Justin	Fiona & Sam Doswell	Zara Fardell
Phil Constable	Datlen	Ian Dougherty	Lana Farrell
Leanne Cook	Joyce Datlen	Paul Dougherty	Claire Fay
Iona Cooke	Liza Datlen	Matt Doulton	Katy Fear
Jenny Cooke	Sarah Datlen	Amy Dovey	Sally Fear
Kevin Cookson	Stuart Datlen	Jaime D'Ovidio	Sarah Fear
Lesley Cookson	Abi Davey	Helen Down	Alice Fee
Natasha Coombes	Louise Davies	Nathan Down	Michael Fellows
Victoria Coombs	Vicky Davies	Tricia Downing	James Fenemore
Charlotte Cooper	Anna Davis	Emma Doyle	Trudy Ferguson
Helen Cooper	Jenny Davis	Kath Drake	Theresa Ferris
Jenni Cooper	Kim Davis	Victoria Drake	Amy Fidler
Rebecca Cooper	Livvie Davis	Jo Drury	Lynn Fidler
Sharon Cooper	Tim Davis	Kirsten Duell	Michelle Fielden
Deborah Cossins	Adrienne Davison	Annette Dunham	Hilary Fielder
Georgi Cottrell	Amanda Dawkins	Maddy Dunlop	Tracy Fife
Julie Coughlan	Steve Dawn	Debbie Durrant	Graham Finch
Helen Court	Mark Dawson	Andrew Dyer	Suzanne Findley
Emma Courtney	Jenni Day	Vicki Eades	Tim Fisher
Karen Cousens	Rosie Day	Madeleine Eardley	Anna Fisk
Samantha Coward	Jan Deakin	Ian Earles	Lucy Fitzgerald
Hannah Cowell	Jayne Denton	Carol Earnshaw	Bridget Flahavan
Harry Coxhead	Samantha De	Sarah Eckton	Kathryn Fletcher
Jack Coxhead	Retuerto	Harry Edwards	Alice Flood
Sharon Craddock	Caroline Devlin	Kim Edwards	Caroline Flood
Hollie Craggs	Marie Devlin	Sharon Edwards	Scott Flood
Jonathan Craner	Abi Dew	Ian Elford	Annebeth Flynn
Sophie Crocket	Kelly Dewey	Sophie El-kindy	James Flynn
Samantha Crockett	Gemma Dewdney	Sam Elliott	Nikki Folland
Laura Crompton	Rachel Drew	Helen Ellis	Beth Foord
Emma Cron	Rebecca Dibben	Laura Ellison	Wendy Foord
Hazel Cross	Amy Dibden	Souad Elmi Djibril	Amanda Ford
Jade Crouch	Emily Dickens	Lisa Else	Gareth Ford
Eddie Croucher	Andrew Dickenson	Eileen Emery	Vanessa Ford
Erin Cuffley	Alice Dickinson	Hayley England	Charlotte Forder
Emma Cullen	Andrea Dixon	Lynn England	Nichola Foster
Sandie Cunningham	Gemma Dixon	Jo English	Alison Fowler

Lorraine Fox
Rachel Fox
Nick Frampton
Esther Franklin
Milly Franklin
Linda Franks
Bridgette Fraser
Wayne Freebody
Emma Freeman
Laura Frostick
Charlotte Fry
Anya Fulford
Jenny & David Fulton
Laura Fulwell-Smith
Jason Futter
Denise Gaden
Naomi Gain
Kay Gale
Shelley Gale
Heather Gambie
Claire Garrett
Dean Garrett
Sally Garrett
Anna Gary
Caroline Gates
Nick Gates
Vicky Gatfield
Sarah Gay
Sandy Gayton
Jim Gerrard
Nin Ghag
Laura Glibbery
Geoffrey Gibbs
Molly Gibbs
Rachel Gibbs
Lucy Giddings
Amber Gigg
Caroline Gigg
India Gigg
Emma Giles
Susan Gill
Katherine Glanville
Charlotte Glasspool
Laura Glibbery
N Godwin

Callum Gohrisch
Lis Gohrisch
Caroline Golding
Jo Goldspink
Gina Gomme
Jan Goodall
Paul Goodall
Ben Goodchild
Toni Goodchild
Rachel Gorfin
David Gorman
Nicky Gossage
Laura Grant
Caitlin Gray
Tamira Gray
Fiona Green
Jeremy Green
Judi Green
Roger Green
Sara Green
Karen Greenaway
Julie Gregory
Emily Griffiths
Hannah Griffiths
Leanne Griffiths
Marie Griffiths
Neil Griffiths
Terry Griffiths
Tracy Griffiths
Kelvin Grimes
Donna Groom
Lin Grout
Matthew Grubb
Teresa Gubbins
Sarah Guilder
Peter Gulliver
Laura Guy
Nicky, Freddie,
Charlotte & Andy
Gynane
Tina Gynane
Helen H
Abbie Haddon-
Mawer
Jamie Hague

Rachel Hailey
Claire Halcrow
Kim Hall
Lindsey Hall
Natalie Hall
Rachael Hall
Tasha Halsey
Kerry Hamilton
Chris Hammond
Elaine Hammond
Sandy Hammond
Claire Hampson
Ian Hampson
Lesley Hampson
Joanne Hancock
Jane Hanley
Paula Hanley
Therese Hanley
Beryl Hannaford
Rachel Hansford
Rebecca Hanson
Sophie Hanspal
Rebecca Harbach
Sarah Harding
Gillian Hargreaves
Donna Harland
Thomas Harper
Amelia Harris
Carolyn Harris
Debbie Harris
Eileen Harris
Emma Harris
Kimberley Harris
Martin Harris
Teresa Harris
Becky Harrison
Dan Harrison
Kat Harrison
Stacey Harrison
Jane Hart
David Hartley
Dianne Harvey
Helen Harvey
Vicki Harvey
Tamara Hatch

Lyn Hatchett
Margaret Hawkes
David & Hilary
Hawkins
Gillian Hawkins
Sally Hawkins
Sue Hawkins
Angie Hayes
Rebecca Hayes
Charlotte Hayter
Linda Hazelwood-
Smith
Denise Headon
Raymond Healy
Julie Hearnden
Deana Heasell
Charlotte Hebburn
Marie Hedley
James & George
Heffer
Rachel Heffernan
Chris Hendley
Sarah Hendley
Caroline Heron
Louise Heslop
Suzanne Hicks
Jonathan Hibberd
Lesley Hibberd
Martha Hibberd
Ashleigh Hill
Jacky Hill
Wendy Hill
Sanita Hillary
Trevor Hillary
Carol Hilton
Charlie & Molly
Himsworth
Julia Hinton
Jo Hipkiss
Gemma Hirst
Annie Hiscock
David Hiscock
Patricia Hiscock
Lesley Hobbs
Iain Hockings

Sarah Hodge	Catherine Jackson	Michelle Kelly	Susan Lane
Sarah Hodges	Jenny Jackson	Heidi Kemp	Sian Langer
Louise Hodgkins	Peter C Jackson	Scott Kempsey	Jill Langford
Sarah Hodgkinson	Ruth Jackson	Carly Kendell	Hang Ching Lau
Caroline Hodgson	Philip Jarvis	Helen Kendrick	Samantha Law
Danielle Hodgson	Jennifer Jefferies	Lisa Kennedy	Deborah Lawrence
Emma Holder	Sharon Jellicoe	Vivienne Kenny	Sarah Lawrence
Claire Holland	Lauren Jenkin	Cliff Kent	Karen Lawrence
Karen Holland	Linda & Tony Jenkin	Maddy Kent	Naomi Layfield
Sophie Holley	Carlene Jenkins	Stevie Kent	Fiona Leagas
Steve Hollick	Claire Jenkinson	Amanda Kenway	Tracey Leddington
Janet Holliday	Andrew Jennings	Deb Kie	Naomi Ledwich
Sam Hollins	Oliver Jennings	Maddie Kilburn	Katrina Lee
Christine Hollis	Katie Johnson	Becki Killham	Maureen & Joe Lee
Emily Holloway	Rebecca Johnson	Debra King	Tammy Lee
Boo Holmquest	Sarah Johnston	Julia King	Bryony Lee-
Gloria Hooper	Terri Johnson	Karen King	Newnham
Jim Hooper	Daniel Jones	Paul King	Emma Le Huray
Bob Horton	Donna Jones	Samantha King	Tanya Leonard
Helen Horton	Emma Jones	Michael Kingdon	Yvonne Leonard
Kay Horton	Hannah Jones	Oliver Kingdon	Katy Le Poidevin
Michael Horton	Kerrie Jones	Jane Kitchen	Karen Lepora
Eleanor Houghton	Maria Jones Funeral	Bob Kitcher	Heather Levy
Lisa Houghton	Directors	Louise Kitcher	Ann Lewin
Emma How	Rachel Jones	Helen Klaassen	Chloe Lewis
Sue Howells	Siobhan Jones	Damen Knappett	Chris Lewis
Sarah Huartson	Vicki Jones	Julie Knechtel	Dave & Sue Lewis
Caroline Hubbard	Nick & Steph Jordan	Bethany Knight	Deborah Lewis
Hilary Hubbard	Theresa Jordan	Gary Knight	Gemma Lewis
Jennifer Hughes	Rhiannon Joslin	Jemma Knight	Graham Lewis
Jo Hughes	Phil Joyner	Josh Knight	Kelly Lewis
Alicia Humphrey	Laura Judd	Anna Knott	Paul Lewis
Claire Hunt	Stephanie Judd	Theresa	Angela Ley
Bev Hurst	Jim, Jumbo House	Kolaczkowski	Lisa Limburn
Kathy Hurst	Alison Kaines	Edmonda Kovnatore	Angela Linch
Sharon Hurst	Jon Kaines	Karen Kritter	Roxanne Lines
Neil Hussey	Marianne Kamau	Kate Kruger	Alison Little
Alister Hutchin	Sue & Sleem Kavde	Carole Lacey	Steven Littlecott
Sue Hutton	Chrissie Kearney	Ellen Lacey	Maddie Littleton
Glenda Hyde	Jayne Kearney	Darren Laithwaite	Jo Livie
Louise Hyndman	Rebecca Keeping	Jen Lake	Carys Lloyd
Hannah Inayat	Amanda Kelly	David Lambley	Sarah Lloyd
Crystal Irving	Caroline Kelly	Katy Lancaster	Gary Lockhart
Anna Isherwood	Conner Kelly	Martin & Jill Lander	Kathleen Lockyer
Michael Isherwood	Mica Kelly	Joanne Lane	Sharon Lockyer

Maxine Long
Hollie Longman
Keith Longman
Sylvia Longman
Persis Longyear
Chris & Liz Lonnon
Christopher Lonnon
Sharon, Thomas &
Katie Lowe
Mrs Lower
Gemma Lucas
Simon & Patricia
Lush
Nicola Lyle
Anne Lyman
Sara Lyons
Mandy Maher
Fran Mahon
Jeanette Maidment
Louise Maidment
Deborah Malone
Jenni Manley
James Manners
Eileen Mansell
Sharlene Marler
Deryck Marley
Rebecca Mars
A Marsden
Jane Marsh
Ron Marsh
Delyth Marshall
Janet & Richard
Marshall
Lauren Marshall
Lacey Martin
Nicola Martin
Sarah Martin
Thomas Martin
Chris Marwood
Debbie Maskell
Aimee Mason
Rosie Masterman
Nina Masters
Sarah Masterton
Kelly Mathys

Liz Matthews
Zoe Matthews
Carol Mavroidaki
Gemma May
Karena May
Joanna Mayhew
Sarah McArthur
Diane McComb
Atlanta McDermott
Linda McDermott
Nadine McDwyer
Sarah McGaw
Gemma McGlead
Jen McGlead
Elisha McGuire
Vanessa McHugh
Donna McInally
Katie McInnes
Kieran McKay
Paul McKnight
Gemma McLean
Julia McLoughlin
Nicky McMenamin
Chelsea McPhee
Lucy Mead
Claire Meaker
Ali Medway
Lorelei Menzies
Vicki Michael
Suzanne Middleton
Sharon, Kelly,
Thomas & Lois
Mifflin-Ashley
Rebecca Mileham
Wendy Millard
Elizabeth Miller
Hayley Miller
Jo Miller
Lisa Mills
Lucy Mills
Nick Mills
Melanie Mines
Mick Minnock
Mike Minnock
Elisa Mitchell

Lynda Mitchell
Nicky Mitrut
Julie Moat
Sandie Mockett
Steve Moger
Alex Montgomerie
Angela Monks
Liz Moody
Nicky Moore
Paula Moore
Louisa Moorhouse
Nikki Moossun
Pete Morrell
Jacqueline Morris
Sian Morris
Sam Morrison
Rachel Morse
Liz Mould
Sarah Moulin
Celia Moulton
Maz Mory
Sue Mudge
Jeanette Muldoon
Kelvin Munro
Roddy & Hilora
Munro
Debbie Murphy
Emma Murgatroyd
Nichola Musgrove
Su Nandy
Jackie Nash
Julie Nash
Joan Neale
Liz Neate
Amanda Neary
Laura Needle
Laura Neiass
Debbie Neill
Jacqui Neill
Janet Newman
Jo Newman
Nicki Newman
Rob Newman
Georgina Newnham
Amanda Newton

Lucy Nicholas
Eric Nicholls
Terry Nicholls
Cheryl Nikandrou
Carla Nobbs
Mark Noonan
Jacqueline Norman
Louise Norris
Kieran Norum
Mark Norum
Mary & David Noyce
Shelley Noyce
Louise Nyman
Alex O'Brien
Tony O'Connor
Grace O'Dea
Kate O'Dell
Callum O'Driscoll
Sarah Officer
Sue Ogburn
Julie Olden
Christina Oldham
Jeanette Oliver
Karen & Aimee
Oliver
Anita Organ
David Olsen
Mark & Jo Olsen
Steve Olsen
Lucy Orchard
Anita Organ
Tessa Orman
Sally O'Rourke
Rachael Orpin
Jodie Osborne
Linda Osborne
Liz Osborne
lilian Osgood
Holly Over
Beckie Owen
Jenny Packer
Jodie Page
Sue & Sarah Paget
L Pain
Madeleine Pain

Linda Palk
Sandra Palmer
Adrian Parsons
Ann Parsons
David Parsons
Ivan & Pru Parsons
Kirsty Parsons
Ami Partridge
Chloe Partridge
Karen & Dan Pass
Julien Paul
Rachel Paul
Tom Paul
Julie Payne
Lauren Payne
Liz Payne
Richard Payne
Karen Paynter
John Peach
Nina Pearshouse
Sally Pearshouse
Nicola Pearson
Diane Peaty
Emily Penn
Jane Penn
Charlotte Peppard
Julie Perdue
Eva Pereira
Kay Perkins
Stuart Perry
Helen Peters
Erica Phillips
Holly Phillips
Karen Phillips
Andrew Phillipson
Gaynor Picton
Mel Picton
Caroline Pike
Louise Pike
Geoff Pinckney
Kim Pitman
Maria Pitts
Aaron Pitty
Astrida Plenty
Carol Plunkett

Katy Pocock
Nicola Polhill
Sue Pomeroy
Jenny Pond
G H Ponting
Becca Pope
Dorothy Popple
Dot Popple
Bev Poskitt
Zara Pothecary
Laura Poulter
Scott Preston
Emily Price
Laurence Price
Mark Price
Nicky Price
Steve Price
David Prince
Dinah Prince
Lisa Prince
Samantha Prince
Claire Pritchard
Elizabeth Pugh
Liz Pusey
Adrienne Pye
Lisa Quinn
Stacey Rabbetts
Sarah Radford
Cliff & Karen Ralls
Julia Rampton
Debbie Randell
Tony Randles
Pamela Rankin
Victoria Rastall
Kerry Rayner
Anna Raynsford
Emma Reed
Kaylea Reed
Hayley Reeves
Rebecca Reeves
Caren Reid
Julie Reynolds
Kerry & Dom
Reynolds
Aidan Richardson

Claire Richardson
Sue Richardson
Diane Richens
Chris Rider
Julie Ridings
Shelley Ripper
Christopher Rixon
Sue Rixon
Roy Rhodes
Stephen Roach
Andrew Roberts
Leanne Roberts
Stuart Roberts
Ivy Robertson
Katherine Robertson
Andrew Robinson
Brian Robinson
David Robinson
Jodie Robinson
Nick & Tic Robinson
Sarah Robinson
Vanessa Robinson
Emma Rogers
Janet Rogers
Lindsay Rogers
Nicola Rogers
Jasmine Roll
Carly Rooney
Hannah Roper
Emma Rose
Melanie Rosenvinge
Nuala Rosenvinge
Lynn Ross
Paul Ross
Andrew Rossdale
Claire Rossiter
Christina Roux
Stephen Rowe
Sarah Rowlands
Kylie Ryan
Karen Rushby
Anna Rutter
Kelly Rygal
Andrew Saint
Paul Saddington

Mick Salter
Debbie Sanders
Richa Sandhu
Daniele Sandy
Miranda
Sanmuganathan
Cathy Satherley
Anna Satterthwaite
Claire Savage
Karen Savage
Nicky Savage
Tim Savage
Kirsty Saward
Debbie Sawyer
Heather Scorey
Lucy Scott
Sue Scott
Craig Scourfield
Beth Scourfield
Mary Scourfield
Jackie Seabrook
Graham Searle
Keith Searle
Paul Searle
Sabrina Searle
Sami Searle
Sharon Searle
Jordan Self
Bernice Sellwood
Karen Sessions
Sharon Seton
Lesley Severs
Gabrielle Seymour
Michelle Seymour
Stuart Seymour
Catherine Shaw
Emma Shaw
Phill Shaw
Theresa Shawyer
Dellen Sheen
Paul Shelmerdine
Emma Shepherd
Lee Shepherd
Steve Shepherd
Melita Sheppard

Richard Sherin
Katie, Mum, Dad, Emma & Daniel Shields
David Shilling
Mary Shinnick-Norum
Helen Ship
John Shuttleworth
Chloe Sid-Ahmad
Linda & John Simkins
Alexandra Simpson
John Simpson
Ian Sims
Louise Sinde
Rose Slade
Jo Small
Kelly Small
Vanessa Small
Natalie Smart
Abigail Smith
Alison Smith
Alun Smith
Andy & Wendy Smith
Cara Smith
Claire Smith
Clive Smith
Elaine Smith
Elijah & Amelia Smith
Emily Smith
Francesca Smith
Ian Smith
Janice Smith
Jo Smith
Laura Smith
Lucy Smith
Megan Smith
Pat Smith
Polly Smith
Sheila Smith
Sue Smith
Wayne Smith
Alice Smith-Connor

Anna Sneddon
Sylvia Snook
Sonia Soares
Tina Soffe
Barry, Solent Skip Hire
Angela Soto
Steve Spacey
Bonnie Sparks
Pauline Sparkes
Lucy Spedding
Ruby Spedding
Erica Spencer
Laura Spencer
Tracy Spiers
Sadie Spillett
Sarah Spurr
Diane Stafford
Robert Staggs
Ros Stamper
Rachel Standing
Sheena Standring
Julie Stannard
Linda Stansbridge
Chris Steeds
Jason Steel
Joanne Steele
Lucy Steer
Tina Steer
Beccy Stevens
Caroline Stevens
Emma Stevens
Kelly Stevens
Alyssa Stewart
Tracie Stickland
Rob Stickells
Diane Stimson
Lindsay Stock
Nina & Chris Stoddart
Jo Stoker
John Stokes
Hilary Stone
Jill Stone
Jo Stone

Amy Stoyles
Nicola Streader
Dean Street
Steph Street
Kate Stride
Karen Stringer
Lucy Stubbington
Melanie Sturgess
Michelle Sutton
Sarah Sutton
Diane Swain
Mike Swann
Sarah Symes
Melissa Taiani
Jenny Tait
Sarah Tapp
Joanne Tattersall
Julie Tattersall
Julie Taylor
Lindsey Taylor
Maurice Taylor
Sharron Taylor
Kirsty Tegg
Daniel Tejada
Claire Terrill
Lucy Tessem
Kim Thackeray
Vikkie Theobald
Gill Thirlwell
Courtney Thomas
Elizabeth Thomas
Hazel Thomas
Kelly Thomas
Michael Thomas
Paul Thomas
Stephen Thomas
Bethany Thomson
David Thompson
Isobel Thompson
Jane Thorne
Rebecca Thorne
Kevin Thorp
Sian Thorp
Katie Timms
Catherine Tipper

Annette Todhunter
Karen Tomlin
Donald Toomer
Donna Tones
Katie Toomer
Mark Topham
Elaine Torrington
Keren Townend
Dawn Townsend
Nicole Townsend
Wendie Travers
Tarina Tribe
Jane Trillo
Claire Tromans
Hannah Trotter
Emma True
Kim Tucker
Jen Turner
Karen Turner
Tracy Turner
George Turton
Emma Tweedie
Michelle Twigg
Martin Tyrrell
Julie Udell
Vicky Underwood
Lisa Upham
Tracey Upward
Robert Usher
Amanda Van Den Berg
Ali Vandyken
Dylan Varndell
Julia Vaughan
Chris Vincent
Donna Vokes
Petra Vollrath
Becky Vonlandau
Neil Wadmore
Neave Wagstaffe
Veronica Wagstaffe
Carol Waite
Nicky Waite
Andy Walker
Deborah Walker

Liz Walker
Mary Jacqueline Walsh
Katie Walton
Charlotte Warburton
Alison Ward
Jenny Ward
Jo Ward
Rebecca Ward
Ali Wareham
Rose & Colin Wareham
Gill Waring
Sherri Warn
Corinne Warwick
Deborah Wassell
Ebony Wateridge
Jackie Wateridge
Gary Watling
Eleanor Watson
Elizabeth Watson
Tom Watson
Christine Watts
Roger & Jean Watts
Samantha Weatherdon
Linzi Weatherson
Amanda Webb
Elisabeth Webb
Elisha Webber
Euan Webster
Lorraine Weeks
Anna Weglarek
Karen Welford
Steph Wells
Tracy Wenczka
Chloe West
Emma West
Josh West
Lucas West
Hayley Weston
Margaret Weston
Elizabeth Whicher
Mandy Whitcher
Brenda White

Eilidh White
Jane White
Karen White
Sue White
William White
Joanna Whitney
Lee Whittaker
Alison Whittick
Alan Whymark
Barbara Wigelsworth
Rebecca Wigglesworth
Jenny Wilcox
Jennifer Wilding
Sharon Wildman
Sam Wilkins
Stewart Wilkins
Cathy Willcocks
Julia Willcocks
Sarah Willes
David Williams
Dean Williams
Debbie Williams
Kerry Williams
Paul Williams
Richard Williams
Sarah Williams
Sharon Williams
Zoe Williams
Sharon Williamson
Robert Willington
Linda Willis
Rebecca Willis
Christie Willmore
Andy Wilson
Anna Wilson
Jenaya Wilson
Emma Wiltshire
Beverley Winch
Kathryn Windibank
Belinda Wing
Trevor Winstanley
Ann Winter
Bev Wiseman
Linda Wiseman

Natasha Wiseman
Mark Witt
Rachel Witts
Catherine Wood
Debbie Wood
Joel Wood
Kim Wood
Ryan Wood
Amanda Wooding
Julia Woodward
Clare Workman
Jamie Wort
Rosamund Wort
Julia Wright
Samantha Wright
Stefanie Wright
Lesley Wyles
Sam Wyne
Sarah Wyne
Carly Yates
Clark Young
Daniel Young
Geoff & Jill Young
Kate Young
Katey Young
Lucy Young
Natasha Young
Russell Young
Gill Younger
Gemma Zammit
Vivien Zhou

Boo & family
Connie & Lois

We're very sorry if you donated and we've somehow missed your name. Do please let us know if this is the case.